RISING STARS
Maths

Problem Solving and Reasoning

Tim Handley

Rising Stars UK Ltd, part of Hodder Education, an Hachette UK Company,
Carmelite House, 50 Victoria Embankment, London, EC4Y 0DZ
www.risingstars-uk.com

Published 2014

Reprinted 2014, 2015 (three times)

Author: Tim Handley

Consultant: Cherri Moseley

Publisher: Fiona Lazenby

Project Manager: Sarah Garbett

Editorial: Jan Fisher, Ethel Chitagu, Bruce Nicholson

Cover design: Words & Pictures Ltd

Design: Words & Pictures Ltd

Typesetting: Sg Creative Services

Illustrations: Tomek Giovanis

CD-ROM development: Alex Morris

British Library Cataloguing in Publication Data.
A CIP record for this book is available from the British Library.

ISBN: 978-1-78339-176-9

Printed by: Ashford Colour Press Ltd, Gosport, Hants

MIX
Paper from responsible sources
FSC® C011748

Acknowledgements

The authors and publishers would like to thank the staff and pupils at the following schools who trialled the *Problem Solving and Reasoning* resources and provided material for the Case Study conversation snippets across the series:

Bentley CEVC Primary School, Bentley, Ipswich

Bignold Primary School and Nursery, Norwich

Copdock Primary School, Copdock, Suffolk

Cutnall Green First School, Cutnall Green, Worcs

Delce Junior School, Rochester, Kent

Ditchingham Primary School, Ditchingham, Suffolk

Donington Cowley Endowed Primary School, Donington, Lincs

Eccleston C E Primary School, Chester, Cheshire

Garden Suburb Junior School, London

Gillingham ST Michael's Primary School, Gillingham, Beccles, Suffolk

Hapton CE VC Primary School, Hapton, Norwich

Harleston CEVA Primary School, Harleston, Norfolk

Piddle Valley CE VA First School, Piddletrenthide, Dorchester, Dorset

St Barnabas CE Primary, Warrington

St Francis de Sales Catholic Junior School, Walton, Liverpool

St Nicholas CE Primary, Hurst, Reading, Berkshire

St. Martha's Catholic Primary School, Kings Lynn, Norfolk

Well Lane Primary School, Birkenhead, Wirral

Woodlands Primary Academy, Great Yarmouth, Norfolk

Worfield Endowed Church of England Primary School, Worfield, Bridgnorth, Shropshire

Microsoft, Windows and PowerPoint are registered trademarks of Microsoft Corporation in the United States and/or other countries.
Formulator Tarsia © 2003-2014 Hermitech Laboratory
Minecraft ®/TM & © 2009-2013 Mojang / Notch

Contents

Introduction

Rising Stars Maths *Problem Solving and Reasoning*

This resource is designed to help teachers develop a 'reasoning classroom' where problem solving and reasoning forms an integral part of each maths lesson. It provides key strategies to help teachers achieve this, together with extended investigation activities.

Problem solving and reasoning in the 2014 curriculum

The aims of the 2014 National Curriculum for Mathematics place a significant emphasis on the development of children's problem-solving and reasoning skills. Below are the aims of the curriculum, with the key elements relating to problem solving and reasoning underlined.

"The national curriculum for mathematics aims to ensure that all pupils:

- become **fluent** in the fundamentals of mathematics, including through varied and frequent practice with increasingly complex problems over time, so that pupils develop conceptual understanding and the ability to recall and apply knowledge rapidly and accurately.

- **reason mathematically** by following a line of enquiry, conjecturing relationships and generalisations, and developing an argument, justification or proof using mathematical language

- can **solve problem**s by applying their mathematics to a variety of routine and non-routine problems with increasing sophistication, including breaking down problems into a series of simpler steps and persevering in seeking solutions.

Mathematics is an interconnected subject in which pupils need to be able to move fluently between representations of mathematical ideas. The programmes of study are, by necessity, organised into apparently distinct domains, but pupils should make rich connections across mathematical ideas to develop fluency, mathematical reasoning and competence in solving increasingly sophisticated problems."

These aims extend problem solving and reasoning beyond simple worded problems, and it is expected that they will form a key part of the new statutory assessments at both KS1 and KS2.

Within the Programmes of Study, very few statements specifically related to problem solving and reasoning statements are provided. To help teachers develop a range of problem solving skills, suggested objectives have been developed and are provided on pages 14 and 15. For this reason, it is important that, when planning maths lessons, teachers always keep the aims of the curriculum in mind and incorporate problem-solving and reasoning opportunities into every lesson.

About the author

Tim Handley

Tim is the Mathematics and ICT Subject Leader at Woodlands Primary Academy, Great Yarmouth, Norfolk and is a Mathematics Specialist Teacher. He is also an accredited NCETM Professional Development Lead (Primary) – one of only a handful of classroom teachers with this status. He has a deep-seated passion for ensuring all children develop a true conceptual understanding of mathematics.

The publishers and authors would like to thank the children and staff at Woodlands Primary Academy for their support in developing these resources

How to use the resources

Structure

The resource is split into two sections:

1 *Key strategies*

2 *Activities and investigations*

At the back of the book you will also find a glossary of useful mathematical terms. All the supporting resources, including editable PowerPoint problem posters and Word files of the Resource Sheets can be found on the CD-ROM that accompanies this Teacher's Book.

Key strategies

This section provides 14 constructs or routines which can be used to integrate problem solving and reasoning into every maths lesson. Each Key Strategy is accompanied by a full explanation, tips for its use and a number of different examples of how the strategy could be used in different areas of mathematics to develop reasoning.

The examples provided are drawn from many areas of the mathematics curriculum. They are intended as starting points, which can then be taken and developed to use in all areas of mathematics.

Each strategy also contains a conversation snippet from a case study from the schools where these resources have been trialled.

Note that the content of some examples is pitched slightly below the equivalent year content objectives in the Programme of Study. This is to allow children to focus on the development of their **reasoning skills**, using subject knowledge with which they are already familiar.

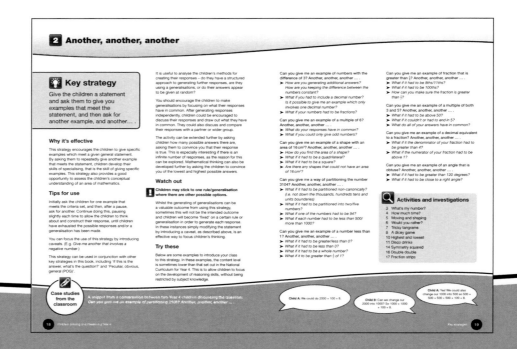

Activities and investigations

This section provides 18 extended problem-solving activities. These all develop one or more key problem-solving and reasoning skills, as well as covering an area of the 2014 National Curriculum. Each activity will last a minimum of one hour and can in many cases, be developed further. The resources for each activity comprise:

- A poster to display on the interactive whiteboard to introduce the problem to the children. This includes the background to the problem, the main challenge or challenges, plus 'Things to think about' prompts to help develop children's reasoning skills. Where appropriate, definitions of any key mathematical terms are also included. Full colour versions of the posters can be found on the accompanying CD-ROM as editable PowerPoint files. They are also reproduced in The problem section of the teacher guidance for ease of reference. Some of the PowerPoint presentations include additional poster slides that can be used to aid differentiation by providing easier and harder versions of the problem.

- Detailed teacher guidance, which includes a learning objective, curriculum links, background knowledge and a step-by-step teaching sequence. The guidance also provides key questions to help develop reasoning (which use one of more of the Key Strategies). Ideas of how to adapt the activity for those that require further support and how the activity could be extended to meet the needs of more able mathematicians are also included.

- For some of the problems, additional Resource sheets that may be useful for the problem are provided on the CD-ROM.

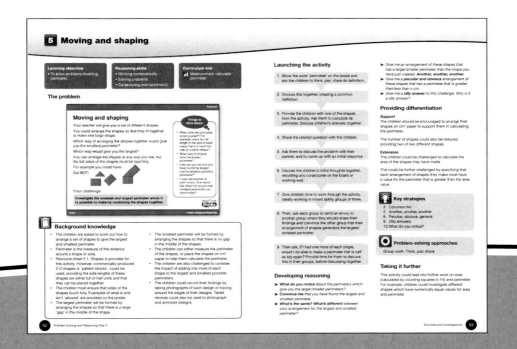

Maths superpowers ^{CPD}

John Mason[1] has identified a set of 8 'Mathematical Powers' that all children possess and which we need to foster and develop in order to create 'able mathematicians' who are able to reason about maths and problem solve. The powers, which come in pairs, are as follows:

Conjecture
Children should be encouraged to **make conjectures**, that is say what they think about what they notice or why something happens. For example, a conjecture made by a child could be, 'I think that when you multiply an odd number by an even number you are always going to end up with an even number'.

and

Convince
Children should then be encouraged to **convince**, that is to persuade people (a partner, group, class, you, an adult at home, etc.) that their conjectures are true. In the process of convincing, children may use some, or all, of their other 'maths powers'.

Organise
Children should be encouraged to **organise**, putting things (numbers, facts, patterns, shapes) into groups, in an order or a pattern, e.g. sorting numbers or shapes.

and

Classify
Children should then be encouraged to **classify** the objects they have organised, e.g. identifying the groups as odd and even numbers, irregular and regular shapes, etc.

Imagine
Children should be encouraged to imagine objects, patterns, numbers and resources to help them solve problems and reason about mathematics.

and

Express
Children should be encouraged to **express their thinking**, that is to show and explain their thinking and reasoning, e.g. about a problem, relationship or generalisations.

Specialise
Children should be encouraged to **specialise**, that is to look at specific examples or a small set of examples of something. For example, looking at the odd number 7 and the even number 8 to test their conjecture that an odd X even number = odd number. Children can also specialise in order to start to see patterns and relationships and make generalisations.

and

Generalise
Children should be encouraged to **generalise**, that is to make connections and use these to form rules and patterns. For example, from their specific example they could generalise that any odd number multiplied by any even number gives an even number. Children should also be encouraged to use algebra to express their generalisations.

These 'maths superpowers' have become the central foundation of many maths teacher development programmes, including the Mathematics Specialist Teacher (MaST) programme.

[1] Mason, J. and Johnston-Wilder,S (eds) (2004 a) Learners Powers in: *Fundamental Constructs in Education*, London:Routledge Falmer pp 115-142

Developing reasoning CPD

Reasoning and conceptual understanding

Encouraging children to reason in maths helps to support children to develop a conceptual and relational understanding of maths: an understanding of **why** maths 'works', rather than just following a set of instructions. This leads to a far greater understanding and confidence in maths.

Developing a reasoning classroom

1   Initially begin by choosing a few of the *Key Strategies* provided in the first section of this resource and introducing them to your class. Many of these strategies, such as **Always, sometimes, never, Peculiar, obvious, general** and **What's the same? What's different?** can also be extended to form whole lessons in their own right, which may be useful when children first experience the strategy.

2   Allow the strategies to form part of your day-to-day questioning, so that children become familiar with using them. If these routines are used regularly, children will quickly get used to structuring their thoughts in this way.

3   Then begin to use the extended problems in the *Activities and Investigations* section. These provide opportunities for children to develop their reasoning skills over a prolonged activity. Each activity includes suggestions of how the *Key Strategies* could be incorporated to develop children's thinking as they work on the investigations.

Cross-curricular reasoning

Of course, children's natural ability to reason extends beyond mathematics. *The Key Strategies* and approaches explained in this resource can easily be used across the curriculum. For example, in a geography-based lesson the question ***What's the same and what's different*** *about these two settlements?* could be asked. Alternatively, in an English lesson children could be asked to identify the **Odd one out** of a selection of words.

Problem-solving techniques ^{CPD}

The following offers a number of suggestions that are useful to consider when organising and supporting children to encourage reasoning in the classroom.

USE ME

When supporting children in problem solving and reasoning activities, the following stages, which form the 'USE ME' mnemonic are useful to follow.

- **U**nderstanding: Check that children understand the problem, activity or statement that has been given. Does it need re-wording or further explanation? Do they have the subject knowledge needed?

- **S**pecialising: Start by asking children to specialise by looking at, or creating, one specific example. This then can be extended to looking at/creating a small group of examples. By specialising, children are more likely to be able to explore the structure of the mathematics, before widening out to make connections and generalisations.

- **E**ncouraging representations: The use of representations is vital as they significantly enhance children's experience and understanding of mathematics. Representations can take many forms including Practical (apparatus such as bead strings, counters, cubes, etc), Recording/Jottings (such as number lines) and Internal (internalised versions of representations that children visualise and imagine). Children should also be encouraged to create their own representations. Encourage children to think about how they could represent the statement, or how they could represent specific examples of the statement.

- **M**aking generalisations: After children have looked at, and often represented, specialised examples, they can begin to explore the connections between their examples. Can they make a statement that applies to all examples? If no generalised statement is possible, can they make a statement that applies to some examples (and define which examples this applies to)? Can they explain why it is not possible to make a generalisation?

- **E**xtending: Provide a further, linked, question or investigation for children to explore.

Grouping for problem solving and reasoning

Teachers often ask how it is best to group children for problem solving and reasoning tasks. Variety is really the key here! Below are some forms of groups for you to consider:

- **Familiar maths partners** who children work with frequently in maths and with whom they are able to communicate well.

- **Pairs of friends** who enjoy working together.

- **Mixed-ability pairs or groups** which have often been shown to raise attainment for all children in the group: the lower-attaining children benefit from the peer coaching from the higher-attaining children, whilst the higher-attaining children have to extend their understanding and thinking further in order to explain it clearly to others.

- **Same-ability pairs or groups** also, of course, have their place, as they allow the task to be closely matched to the children's ability

It is important that children become used to working in different types of groups. In this way, they develop increasing flexibility and become adept at explaining their thinking and reasoning to a wide range of people. Different tasks will, of course, suit different ways of grouping.

Panic envelopes to facilitate self-differentiation

These are a great strategy to enable self-differentiation of problem-solving and reasoning activities. Inside an envelope, place one or more items that will support the children in carrying out the activity, then place the envelopes either in the middle of a group's table and/or on a maths working wall.

The content of the envelopes can be varied, and could include:

- Additional information

- Key questions to help develop thinking

- Conjectures for the children to prove/disprove

- Specific examples

- Partly or fully worked solutions to part of the problem

Give children the challenge of taking part in the activity independently, but let them know that at any point during the activity they can self-select to open the panic envelope and read one or more of the items that you have placed inside. Of course, adults in the classroom can also suggest to children that they may benefit from opening the 'panic envelope' if they become stuck while working through an activity. The content of the envelopes can be further differentiated for different groups of children.

Graffiti maths

Graffiti maths is an approach to problem solving and reasoning tasks which encourages children to think and work 'big'. It was developed almost simultaneously by a number of teachers, including Claire Lotriet and Geoff Barton in 2012 .

Graffiti maths involves children working together as a team on a problem or investigation, working on tables that are covered in 'magic whiteboard' sheets, large pieces of paper (taped down) or another covering which allows children to write 'on' the tables. Some teachers also choose to remove the chairs from the classroom, which encourages children to move around the table.

This approach encourages children to work together and gives them ample space to explore ideas, test out conjectures and make connections. The recording space is shared, which means that one child is less likely to take 'ownership' of it whilst others hang back and 'lurk' in the background. The act of sharing the recording space also encourages maths talk and creates a generally 'buzzy' atmosphere in your classroom.

Children can also move around and look at different tables and their recording, which can be a very useful plenary or mid-session activity.

Think, pair, share

This strategy is particularly effective during shared learning. This is a development of 'simple' paired talk. Ask a question (usually open-ended) and give children a period of thinking time (normally one to two minutes works best) for them to 'privately' think about the question or problem posed. Next, give children some time to discuss the question/thinking with a partner, before the partners share their thinking with another pair (so forming groups of four).

Envoy

This technique enables ideas to be shared between different groups. Having given children time to discuss their own thoughts, conjectures and generalisations in groups, each group then sends an 'envoy' to share their discussions with another group.

The envoy could be chosen by the group, or be selected by the teacher. By randomly selecting the envoy, you will help each group ensure that every child in the group understands the thinking, conjectures or generalisations of the group as any one of them may be called upon to explain them to another group.

As a further extension, the envoy can be asked to bring back a summary of the thoughts from the group they visited to their 'Home' group, so that the groups can consider new ideas and revisit their own thinking in light of the other conjectures.

[2] http://clairelotriet.com/blog/2012/12/15/graffiti-maths/

Snowballing

After giving time for paired discussion, the discussion can then be 'snowballed'. Ask pairs to share with another pair, and then these groups to snowball together and discuss with another group (forming groups of 8). Depending on class size, this can be repeated again (forming groups of 16) before each of the 'snowballed' groups feeds back to the whole class.

WWW and EBI as a plenary

A useful activity for the plenary session is to ask children **W**hat **W**ent **W**ell (WWW) about the activity and what would be **E**ven **B**etter **I**f (EBI). A ratio of 4 WWWs to 1 EBI is often effective, as this encourages children to focus on the positive and strengths from the session. The phrase of 'even better if …' encourages children to be constructive in their suggestions for improvement. So, rather than 'we didn't work together very well', children might phrase an EBI as 'It would have been **even better if** we had listened more to what each other said so that we could share our thinking together.'

Assessing progress

Accurate assessment of children's problem solving and reasoning skills is only possible through observation of and conversations with the child, together with evidence from their recorded work. The bank of evidence of a child's problem solving and reasoning ability will naturally be built up over time, as children experience and take part in a range of different activities.

The objectives in the chart on the following pages can be used when planning and assessing the problem-solving and reasoning elements of the new curriculum.

Problem solving and reasoning objectives

Year 1	Year 2	Year 3
• Describe a puzzle or problem using numbers, practical materials and diagrams; use these to solve the problem and set the solution in the original context. • Order and arrange combinations of objects and shapes in patterns. • Answer a question by selecting and using suitable equipment, and sorting information, shapes or objects; display results using tables and pictures. • Describe simple patterns and relationships involving numbers or shapes; decide whether examples satisfy given conditions. • Describe ways of solving puzzles and problems, explaining choices and decisions orally or using pictures.	• Identify and record the information or calculation needed to solve a puzzle or problem; carry out the steps or calculations and check the solution in the context of the problem. • Follow a line of enquiry; answer questions by choosing and using suitable equipment and selecting, organising and presenting information in lists, tables and simple diagrams. • Describe patterns and relationships involving numbers or shapes, make predictions and test these with examples. • Present solutions to puzzles and problems in an organised way; explain decisions, methods and results in pictorial, spoken or written form, using mathematical language and number sentences.	• Represent the information in a puzzle or problem using numbers, images or diagrams; use these to find a solution and present it in context, where appropriate using £.p notation or units of measure. • Follow a line of enquiry by deciding what information is important; make and use lists, tables and graphs to organise and interpret the information. • Identify patterns and relationships involving numbers or shapes, and use these to solve problems. • Express the rules for sequences in words (e.g. 3, 5, 7: you add 2 each time). • Begin to make generalisations based on patterns in mathematics (e.g. all even numbers end in either a 0, 2, 4, 6 or 8). • Begin to make conjectures (statements) about mathematics and develop the ability to convince others (e.g. when continuing a pattern). • Begin to make 'if...then...' statements (e.g. if 2 + 4 = 6 then 6 − 2 = 4). • Describe and explain methods, choices and solutions to puzzles and problems, orally and in writing, using pictures and diagrams.

Year 4	Year 5	Year 6
• Represent a puzzle or problem using number sentences, statements or diagrams; use these to solve the problem; present and interpret the solution in the context of the problem.	• Represent a puzzle or problem by identifying and recording the information or calculations needed to solve it; find possible solutions and confirm them in the context of the problem.	• Tabulate systematically the information in a problem or puzzle; identify and record the steps or calculations needed to solve it, using symbols where appropriate; interpret solutions in the original context and check their accuracy.
• Suggest a line of enquiry and the strategy needed to follow it; collect, organise and interpret selected information to find answers.	• Plan and pursue an enquiry; present evidence by collecting, organising and interpreting information; suggest extensions to the enquiry.	• Suggest, plan and develop lines of enquiry; collect, organise and represent information, interpret results and review methods; identify and answer related questions.
• Identify and use patterns, relationships and properties of numbers or shapes; investigate a statement involving numbers and test it with examples.	• Explore patterns, properties and relationships and propose a general statement involving numbers or shapes; identify examples for which the statement is true or false.	• Represent and interpret sequences, patterns and relationships involving numbers and shapes; suggest and test hypotheses; construct and use simple expressions and formulae in words then symbols.
• Express the rules for increasingly complex sequences in words (e.g. 3, 6, 12, 24: you double each time).	• Explain reasoning using diagrams, graphs and text; refine ways of recording using images and symbols.	• Explain reasoning and conclusions, using words, symbols or diagrams as appropriate. Use simple formulae expressed in words. Express missing number problems algebraically (e.g. $6 + n = 28$).
• Report solutions to puzzles and problems, giving explanations and reasoning orally and in writing, using diagrams and symbols.	• Begin to express missing number problems algebraically. (e.g. $6 + n = 12$).	• Begin to use symbols and letters to represent variables (things that can change) and unknowns in mathematics situations which they already understand, such as missing numbers, missing lengths, arithmetical rules (e.g. $a + b = b + a$) and number puzzles (e.g. two numbers total 6, therefore $a + b = 6$).
• Continue to make generalisations based on patterns in mathematics.	• Continue to make increasingly advanced generalisations based on patterns in mathematics.	• Continue to make increasingly advanced generalisations based on patterns in mathematics.
	• Make conjectures (statements) about mathematics and further develop the ability to convince others.	• Make conjectures (statements) about mathematics and further develop the ability to convince others.
	• Continue to make 'if … then …' statements.	• Continue to make 'if … then … ' statements, representing them using letters if able (e.g. if $2 + 4 = 6$, then $6 - 2 = 4$ represented using letters: if $a + b = c$ then $c - a = b$).

Always, sometimes, never

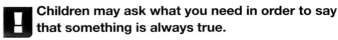 **Key strategy**

Give the children a statement and then ask whether it is always, sometimes or never true.

Why it's effective

This line of questioning encourages children to think about the concept of mathematical proof, and allows them to develop the key skill of proving or disproving a statement. This key strategy is very effective at encouraging children to make connections between different areas of mathematics and for encouraging generalisations and algebraic thinking.

Tips for use

This key strategy makes a particularly effective starter activity. It can also be effective when introducing a new focus or concept. It works particularly well if time is allowed for paired or grouped discussion, with the children encouraged to discuss the statement together and come up with their answer (always, sometimes, never) and justification before feeding back to you or the class. You can play 'devil's advocate', giving the children different examples to check against their decision. It can also work well to give children a statement about which they may have misconceptions (e.g. *multiplication always makes things bigger*).

The strategy can also be used as a powerful assessment tool by asking the same 'always, sometimes, never' question at the start and end of the unit. Through doing this you should be able to notice and evidence the increased sophistication in the children's thinking and reasoning skills.

Children can also be given sets of statements to sort into 'always true', 'sometimes true' or 'never true'. These statements could be from one area of mathematics (e.g. *all about fractions*) or a mixture of areas. The activity can also be extended to ask how the statements can be changed to make the always true, sometimes true or never true.

Children should also be encouraged to move towards generalised statements and, if they are able, algebraic representations of their answer, especially when the statement is 'always true'.

Watch out

Children may ask what you need in order to say that something is always true.

This can be used as a really effective discussion point about the nature of mathematical proof. Ask: *How many examples do you need to give to prove a statement is not true? What do you need to do to prove a statement is always true?*

Try these

Below are some examples to introduce your class to this strategy. In these examples, the content level is sometimes lower than that set out in the National Curriculum for Year 4. This is to allow children to focus on the development of reasoning skills, without being restricted by subject knowledge.

Is it always, sometimes or never true that the product of two even numbers is even?
➤ *Let's multiply some even numbers together … what do you notice?*
➤ *Why is this?*
➤ *What happens when you are multiplying? Could we write down the multiplication as repeated addition?*
➤ *What do we know about what happens when you add an even number to an even number?*

Case studies from the classroom

A snippet from a conversation between two Year 4 children discussing the question: *Is it always, sometimes or never true that multiplication makes a number bigger?*

Is it always, sometimes or never true that a number has at least two factor pairs?

➤ Can you find some numbers which do not have two factor pairs?
➤ If appropriate, extend by asking: *What do we call these numbers?*

Is it always, sometimes or never true that when you multiply a number by 10, you add a 0 onto the end?
➤ Can we write down some multiplication sentences which involve multiplying by 10?
➤ What appears to be happening?
➤ Where does the 0 come from? (Ensure children are aware that 0 is acting as a place holder.)
➤ Can we find an example where a 0 does not get added onto the end of the number?
➤ What happens if we multiplied 1.3 × 10?

Is it always, sometimes or never true that rectangles with the largest perimeters have the biggest areas?
➤ Can we draw some rectangles on squared paper? What are the areas and perimeters of these rectangles?

Is it always, sometimes or never true that multiplication makes things bigger?
➤ Can you think of any multiplication you could do that would not make your starting number bigger?
➤ What happens if you multiply by a 1 or 0?

Is it always, sometimes or never true that every fraction has at least one fraction that is equivalent to it?
➤ Can you list some fractions that are equivalent to each other?
➤ How can you find equivalent fractions?

Is it always, sometimes, or never true that a quadrilateral has a line of symmetry?
➤ Can we draw some quadrilaterals? Do all of the quadrilaterals you have drawn so far have at least one line of symmetry?
➤ Can you draw an irregular quadrilateral that does not have a line of symmetry?
➤ Do all irregular quadrilaterals have no lines of symmetry?

Is it always, sometimes, or never true that a bar chart is the best way of displaying data?
➤ How else could you display data?
➤ When would a bar chart be good for displaying data?
➤ If you had data that changed over time, would a bar chart still be the best way to show this data?

Is it always, sometimes or never true that the perimeter of a shape is always an even number?
➤ How do you find the perimeter of a shape?
➤ What do we know about adding numbers together? (odd + odd = even etc.)
➤ Which shapes would this statement always/never be true for?
➤ What if one or more sides has a length that is not a whole number?

 Activities and investigations

8   A dicey game
10 Highest and lowest
17 Fraction strips

Child A: Well, all the ones I've tried so far do, so it must be always.

Child B: Let's think more though, what about if you multiplied a decimal number?

Key strategy

Give the children a statement and ask them to give you examples that meet the statement, and then ask for another example, and another … .

Why it's effective

This strategy encourages children to give specific examples which meet a given general statement. By asking them to repeatedly give another example that meets the statement, children develop their skills of specialising, that is the skill of giving specific examples. This strategy also provides a good opportunity to assess children's conceptual understanding of an area of mathematics.

Tips for use

Initially ask the children for one example that meets the criteria set, and then, after a pause, ask for another. Continue doing this, pausing slightly each time to allow the children to think about and construct their response, until children have exhausted the possible responses and/or a generalisation has been made.

You can focus the use of this strategy by introducing caveats. (E.g. *Give me another that involves a negative number*.)

This strategy can be used in conjunction with other key strategies in this book, including 'If this is the answer, what's the question?' and 'Peculiar, obvious, general (POG)'.

It is useful to analyse the children's methods for creating their responses – do they have a structured approach to generating further responses, are they using a generalisations, or do their answers appear to be given at random?

You should encourage the children to make generalisations by focusing on what their responses have in common. After generating responses independently, children could be encouraged to discuss their responses and draw out what they have in common. They could also discuss and compare their responses with a partner or wider group.

The activity can be extended further by asking children how many possible answers there are, asking them to convince you that their response is true. This is especially interesting if there is an infinite number of responses, as the reason for this can be explored. Mathematical thinking can also be developed further by asking the children to convince you of the lowest and highest possible answers.

Watch out

 Children may stick to one rule/generalisation where there are other possible options.

Whilst the generating of generalisations can be a valuable outcome from using this strategy, sometimes this will not be the intended outcome and children will become 'fixed' on a certain rule or generalisation in order to generate each response. In these instances simply modifying the statement by introducing a caveat, as described above, is an effective way to focus children's thinking.

Try these

Below are some examples to introduce your class to this strategy. In these examples, the content level is sometimes lower than that set out in the National Curriculum for Year 4. This is to allow children to focus on the development of reasoning skills, without being restricted by subject knowledge.

Case studies from the classroom

A snippet from a conversation between two Year 4 children discussing the question: *Can you give me a way of partitioning 2108? Another, another, another … .*

Can you give me an example of numbers with the difference of 3? Another, another, another … .

➤ *How are you generating additional answers? How are you keeping the difference between the numbers constant?*

➤ *What if you had to include a decimal number? Is it possible to give me an example which only involves one decimal number?*

➤ *What if your numbers had to be fractions?*

Can you give me an example of a multiple of 6? Another, another, another … .

➤ *What do your responses have in common?*

➤ *What if you could only give odd numbers?*

Can you give me an example of a shape with an area of 16 cm²? Another, another, another … .

➤ *How do you find the area of a shape?*

➤ *What if it had to be a quadrilateral?*

➤ *What if it had to be a square?*

➤ *Are there any shapes that could not have an area of 16 cm²?*

Can you give me a way of partitioning the number 3104? Another, another, another … .

➤ *What if it had to be partitioned non-canonically? (i.e. not down the thousands, hundreds tens and units boundaries)*

➤ *What if it had to be partitioned into two/five numbers?*

➤ *What if one of the numbers had to be 94?*

➤ *What if each number had to be less than 500/ more than 1000?*

Can you give me an example of a number less than 1? Another, another, another … .

➤ *What if it had to be greater/less than 0?*

➤ *What if it had to be less than 0?*

➤ *What if it had to be a whole number?*

➤ *What if it to be greater than $\frac{1}{2}$ of 1?*

Can you give me an example of fraction that is greater than $\frac{1}{2}$? Another, another, another … .

➤ *What if it had to be 8ths/11ths?*

➤ *What if it had to be 100ths?*

➤ *How can you make sure the fraction is greater than $\frac{1}{2}$?*

Can you give me an example of a multiple of both 3 and 5? Another, another, another … .

➤ *What if it had to be above 50?*

➤ *What if it couldn't or had to end in 5?*

➤ *What do all of your answers have in common?*

Can you give me an example of a decimal equivalent to a fraction? Another, another, another … .

➤ *What if it the denominator of your fraction had to be greater than 4?*

➤ *What if the numerator of your fraction had to be above 1?*

Can you give me an example of an angle that is obtuse? Another, another, another … .

➤ *What if it had to be greater than 120 degrees?*

➤ *What if it had to be close to a right angle?*

 Activities and investigations

Child A: We could do 2000 + 100 + 8.

Child B: Can we change our 2000 into 1000? So 1000 + 1000 + 100 + 8.

Child A: Yes! We could also change our 1000 into 500 so 500 + 500 + 500 + 500 + 100 + 8.

Key strategy

Make a statement to the children and ask them to decide whether it is accurate or not, then explain their reasoning to convince you.

Why it's effective

This key strategy encourages children to look at the structure of mathematics and is another way for children to explore the concept of mathematical proof. Through trying to convince someone that a statement is true, children will begin to make generalisations and develop their algebraic thinking.

Tips for use

This strategy is particularly effective when the statements given to children are statements which they 'take for granted' and assume are correct. Asking children to convince you that these are true (e.g. *multiplication is commutative, i.e. $6 \times 7 = 7 \times 6$*) will deepen their conceptual understanding of mathematics.

Whilst the strategy can be effectively used with given statements, perhaps the most powerful use of this strategy is in response to children's own statements and can sometimes lead to an impromptu, but valuable, diversion from the planned activity.

The strategy can be used alongside the 'Always, sometimes, never' strategy to help develop and prompt children's thinking.

When supporting children in responding to this strategy, the following 'USE ME' stages are often useful (see page 10 for more detail):

- **Understanding:** do children understand the statement?
- **Specialising:** looking at one, or a small number of examples of the statement.
- **Encouraging representations:** *how could we represent the statement, or our specific examples of the statement?*
- **Making generalisations:** *by looking at our specialised examples, can we begin to make a statement that applies to all examples?*
- **Extending:** provide a further, linked, question for children to explore. This often works well when used in conjunction with other strategies from this book.

Watch out

 Children may respond with 'Because it is … .'

When children are first asked to convince someone that a statement is true, they often respond with a response along the lines of 'Because it is …' or 'Because my teachers have always told me.' Children can be encouraged to respond in the form 'It is true that … because … .

Children may not know where to start.

First check if the children have the required prior knowledge and understanding to be able to convince you that the statement is true. If they do, then providing some initial probing questions, perhaps on 'panic cards' (see Problem-solving techniques on page 11), can help them to follow a line of reasoning.

Try these

Below are some examples to introduce your class to this strategy. In these examples, the content level is sometimes lower than that set out in the National Curriculum for Year 4. This is to allow children to

 **Case studies from the classroom**

A snippet from a conversation between two Year 4 children discussing the question: *Can you convince me that multiplication is commutative?*

focus on the development of reasoning skills, without being restricted by subject knowledge.

Convince me … that multiplication is commutative.
➤ (<u>U</u>nderstanding) *What does commutative mean?*
➤ (<u>S</u>pecialising) *Let's look at an example. How about 7 × 9 which we know is the same as 9 × 7? But why is this the case?*
➤ (<u>E</u>ncouraging representations) *How could we represent a multiplication? Could we show 3 × 4 as an array? So, if we rotated our array* (rotate by 90 degrees) *that shows 3 × 4. What does the array now show?*
➤ (<u>M</u>aking generalisations) *Would this be the same for all multiplication facts? Can we always show a multiplication as an array?*
➤ (<u>E</u>xtending) *Are there any other operations that are commutative?*

Convince me … that multiples of 25 are also multiples of 5.
➤ *Can you give me some examples? Are they multiples of both numbers? Why would multiples of 25 also be multiples of 5?*

Convince me … that 1000 cm = 10 m.
➤ *How many cm are in 1 m?*

Convince me … that some fractions are equivalent.
➤ (<u>U</u>nderstanding and <u>M</u>aking generalisations) *What does equivalent mean? What do we mean when we say fractions are equivalent?*
➤ (<u>S</u>pecialising) *Can you come up with any fractions that are equivalent to each other?*
➤ *Can you use a diagram to help show that these fractions are equivalent?*
➤ (<u>M</u>aking generalisations) *How are these fractions linked? Can you create any other equivalent fractions? Do you have to use a diagram to help you each time?*
➤ (<u>E</u>xtending) *Can you write some fractions equivalent to $\frac{3}{5}$?*

Convince me … that squares are rectangles.
➤ (<u>U</u>nderstanding and <u>M</u>aking generalisations) *What is a rectangle? How can we define a rectangle?* (A rectangle is any shape with four straight sides and four right angles.)
➤ (<u>S</u>pecialising) *Draw me three different squares.*
➤ *So does a square meet the definition of a rectangle?*
➤ (<u>M</u>aking generalisations) *So, could we say that squares are rectangles as they always have four straight sides and four right angles?*
➤ (<u>E</u>xtending) *Could we technically call a square a regular rectangle?*

Convince me … that the product of an odd and even number is always even.
➤ *How else can we show a multiplication?* (repeated addition) *What does an odd number plus an odd number always equal?*

Convince me … that 1 metre is 1000 millimetres.
➤ *How many centimetres are in a metre? How many millimetres are in a centimetre?*

Activities and investigations

Child A: It's true because if you have two questions with the same numbers, like 6 X 4 and 4 X 6, they both come up with the same anwer.

Child A: What do you mean?

Child B: And in the times table grid, there are two times tables with the same answer.

Child B: Well, if you find 4 across the top and 8 down the side, the answer is 32, and if you do it the other way, find 8 at the top and 4 at the side, it's still 32.

Key strategy

Ask the children to give you an example of a 'hard' and 'easy' answer to a question, explaining why one is 'hard' and the other 'easy'.

Why it's effective

This strategy encourages children to think closely about the structure of mathematics and enables them to demonstrate a conceptual understanding of concepts. Children enjoy the challenge of coming up with 'hard' examples that still meet the requirements set out in the question.

The choices children make when responding to this strategy often provides valuable information about what they find difficult, which may not always be what you expect! For example, if a child constantly gives calculations involving decimals as a 'hard' question, then this would probably indicate they are insecure with decimal place value.

Tips for use

Unlike most of the strategies in this book, this strategy generally works best if children are encouraged to respond individually first. Once they have come up with their own 'hard' and 'easy' responses they should then be encouraged to discuss and compare these with a partner or larger group. The strategy 'What's the same? What's different?' can be used here to encourage children to compare and contrast their responses and draw out key themes/concepts.

Children should be encouraged to explain why the examples they have given are 'hard' or 'easy'. This could be by way of a written explanation or by convincing their partner/an adult verbally that their responses are 'hard' or 'easy'.

Watch out

Children may respond to the request for a 'hard' example by giving very large multiples of 10 (e.g. 46,000 + 20,000).

Ask the children to convince you why this is a hard example. Then discuss how this could be made 'easy', e.g. by multiplying/dividing by a multiple of 10 and using known facts (in the example above, $46 + 20 = 66$, $66 \times 1000 = 660,000$).

Try these

Below are some examples to introduce your class to this strategy. In these examples, the content level is sometimes lower than that set out in the National Curriculum for Year 4. This is to allow children to focus on the development of reasoning skills, without being restricted by subject knowledge.

Give me a hard and easy example of a 4-digit addition.
- ➤ *Easy: 1000 + 3000 as both numbers are round numbers*
- ➤ *Hard: 4587 + 3874 as the addition crosses the thousands, hundreds, tens and units boundary*

Give me a hard and easy example of a 4-digit subtraction number sentence.
- ➤ *Easy: 5000 – 3000 as it involves two multiples of 1000 with a small difference*
- ➤ *Hard: 2644 – 1287 as it crosses the tens and units boundaries; 2432 – ? = 1218 as it is not in the 'usual' format for subtraction and involves a missing number*

 Case studies from the classroom

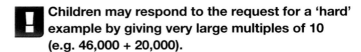 **A snippet from a conversation between two Year 4 children discussing the question:** *Give me a hard and easy example of a multiple of 6 over 100.*

Give me a hard and easy example of a way to partition 3889.

➤ *Easy: 300, 800, 80 and 9 as it is partitioned along the thousands, hundreds, tens and units boundary (canonically)*
➤ *Hard: 1800, 1630, 230, 222, 7 as it is partitioned into five numbers, none of which are 'obvious' within 3889*

Give me a hard and easy example of an equivalent fraction.

➤ *Easy: $\frac{1}{2}$ and $\frac{2}{4}$ as it is simple to spot the equivalence because it is clear that 4 is a multiple of 2 and 2 is a multiple of 1*
➤ *Hard: $\frac{7}{8}$ and $\frac{84}{96}$ as it is not immediately clear that 96 is a multiple of 8 and 84 is a multiple of 7*

Give me a hard and easy example of a sequence of numbers.

➤ *Easy: 2, 4, 6, 8, 10 as it has a single-step rule which is easy to spot* (multiples of 2)
➤ *Hard: 18, 108, 648, 3888 as it has a rule that is not immediately apparent* (×6) *and involves larger numbers*

Give me a hard and easy example of a number to divide by 100.

➤ *Easy: 600 as it is a multiple of 100*
➤ *Hard: 47.3 as it is a decimal number*

Give me a hard and easy example of a fraction of number.

➤ *Easy: $\frac{3}{10}$ of 20 as it uses our known double/half factors*
➤ *Hard: $\frac{9}{17}$ of 119 as it has a non-unit numerator*

Give me a hard and easy example of a two-step question you could ask about this data.

➤ *Easy and hard answers will depend on the data/ chart you provide for the children.* Give me a hard and easy example of a multiple of 6 over 100.
➤ *Easy: 600, as it's a multiple of 100*
➤ *Hard: 738, as it's not a multiple of 10 or 100*

Give me a hard and easy example of a way to measure the width of the school hall.

➤ *Easy: using a trundle wheel*
➤ *Hard: using a classroom ruler*

Activities and investigations

10 Highest and lowest
11 Disco drinks
13 Crack the code
15 Terrific thirty-six
17 Fraction strips

Child A: Well, an easy example would be 600, as that's a multiple of 6 and 100.

Child B: A more difficult one would be something like 390, as it takes a bit of work to prove it's a multiple of 6. But it is, as we know than 300 is a multiple of 6, and 90 is as well, so 390 must be!

Key strategy

Give children an answer and ask them to come up with as many questions as possible that could have that answer.

Why it's effective

This strategy encourages children to think creatively and explore the structure of the numbers and mathematics. Children will begin to spot and use patterns and through this make their own generalisations.

Tips for use

The children should be encouraged to share their possible questions in pairs and collate them together, explaining their possible questions to their partner if needed. Finally, each pair could be invited to share a possible question with the class, picking a question which they think no one else will have come up with. This provides a great opportunity for further questioning, which could incorporate some of the other key strategies, such as 'Convince me', 'Always, sometimes, never', and 'Another, another, another'.

Recording possible questions on a mind map, with the answer in the middle is an effective way to record responses to this key strategy. On-line collective canvases such as lino-it (www.linoit.com) and padlet (www.padlet.com) can also be effective to collaboratively record possible answers.

Children can also be encouraged to put their possible questions into categories. Some obvious categories could be questions related to division, questions which involve an odd number, questions which are in context, etc. However, asking children to categorise their possible questions themselves is often surprising and creates a good opportunity for further discussion.

The strategy can also be easily differentiated by adding set criteria to challenge or support children, e.g. only questions that involve negative numbers, only questions that involve multiplication, etc.

The strategy also provides a great opportunity to encourage children to follow patterns. For example, if a suggested question is 4×8, can they also see that 2×16, 1×32 and 0.5×64 are also possible questions?

Finally the strategy can also work well if it is run as a timed competition. Set a time limit and challenge children to come up with as many possible questions as they can, before then going through some of the follow-up stages suggested above.

Watch out

Children may get stuck with one rule.

Sometimes children will get stuck with one 'rule' or type of question, e.g. addition questions. This can easily be overcome by asking the child to make their next question different: *What about a question involving a fraction? Give me a question involving a decimal number.*

Case studies from the classroom

A snippet from a conversation between two Year 4 children discussing the question: *If the question is 36, what could the possible answer be?*

Try these

Below are some examples to introduce your class to this strategy. In these examples, the content level is sometimes lower than that set out in the National Curriculum for Year 4. This is to allow children to focus on the development of reasoning skills, without being restricted by subject knowledge.

If the answer is 36, what could the possible questions be?
➤ Challenge: *One of your questions must include the same digit twice.*

If the answer is 3, what could the possible questions be?
➤ Challenge: *Your question must include a negative number.*

If the answer is $\frac{3}{4}$, what could the possible questions be?
➤ Challenge: *Your question must be in a context.*

If the answer is 'the tens digit is always even', what could the possible questions be?
➤ Challenge: *One of your questions must be a generalisation.*

If the answer is 9 coaches, what could the possible questions be?
➤ Challenge: *Your question must involve division.*

If the answer is 49 squares, what could the possible questions be?
➤ Challenge: *Your question must involve a square.*

If the answer is a square what could the possible questions be?
➤ Challenge: *Your question must include a generalisation.*

If the answer is 10,000 g, what could the possible questions be?
➤ Challenge: *Your question must refer to kg.*

If the answer is 6, 12, 18, 24 what could the possible questions be?
➤ Challenge: *Your questions must define the sequence in words.*

Activities and investigations

15 Terrific thirty-six
18 Birthdays

Child A: It could be 26 + 10 = ?

Child B: Or 27 + 9 = ?

Child A: We could follow a pattern then: 29 + 8 = ?, 29 + 7 = ?, 30 + 6 = ?, 31 + 4 = ? …

Key strategy

Give the children a number, geometry concept or measure and ask them to write its 'story', that is as much as they know or can work out about it.

Why it's effective

This strategy encourages children to explore everything they know about a mathematical concept and is therefore particularly effective at developing children's subject knowledge whilst also encouraging them to reason.

Through telling a 'story', children are also likely to form and use their own generalisations and patterns, which can be a great starting point for further discussion.

Tips for use

Start by giving children a number (which could include a decimal, fraction, negative numbers and decimals), a geometry concept (e.g. *a shape or co-ordinate*), or a measure (e.g. *an angle*). Then ask children to write as many statements as they can about the item given.

For example, when given a number children may choose to look at the classification of the number (odd, even, prime, square, etc), the factors and multiples of the number, doubling and halving the number, sums and differences that lead to the number, statements that involve proportions of the number, etc.

As children create their 'story' they are likely to create and use their own generalisations and patterns. Discussing these with children using the 'What else do we know?' and 'What do we notice?' key strategies is particularly effective.

This strategy can also work well as an individual or paired activity, followed by a class 'race' to record as many different elements of the numbers 'story' on a interactive whiteboard within a given time limit.

Watch out

Children may focus on one pattern.

Children often get 'locked on' to one pattern, e.g. doubling and halving. Encourage children to explore other patterns by setting a target number of 'unrelated' facts that they record.

Children may 'run out' of facts to record.

Sometimes children will appear to run out of facts to record. Draw children's attention to patterns within what they have recorded so far and ask: *What else do we know?* A bank of prompt questions may also be useful, providing prompts for things to investigate, e.g. *What number is double the number? What are the factors of the number?*

Try these

Below are some examples to introduce your class to this strategy. In these examples, the content level is sometimes lower than that set out in the National Curriculum for Year 4. This is to allow children to focus on the development of reasoning skills, without being restricted by subject knowledge.

Case studies from the classroom

A snippet from a conversation between two Year 4 children discussing the question: *What is the story of 22?*

General prompt questions to use with number-based stories (including fractions and decimals).
- ➤ *What type of number is it?*
- ➤ *What is it a multiple of?*
- ➤ *What are some multiples of the number?*
- ➤ *What factors does it have? Does this mean it is a special type of number?*
- ➤ *Can you write this as a fraction/decimal?*
- ➤ *What is double the number? Double this number?*
- ➤ *What is half the number? Half this number?*
- ➤ *What happens when you multiply the number by 10? 100?*
- ➤ *What happens when you divide the number by 10? 100?*
- ➤ *What can you add together to make this number?*
- ➤ *What calculations could this number be involved in?*

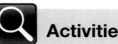 **Activities and investigations**

15 Terrific thirty-six

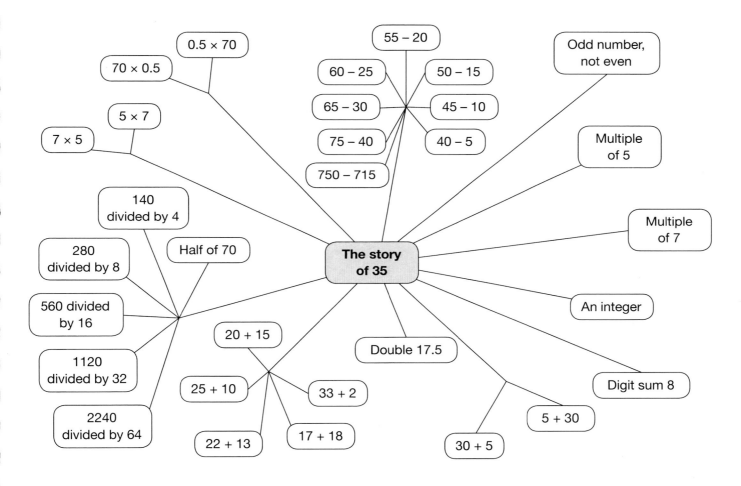

Child A: 22 is a number, and it's even.

Child B: It's half of 44.

Child A: Which must also mean it's a quarter of 88.

7 Odd one out

💡 Key strategy

Give the children a set of three or more numbers or statements and ask them to identify which number/statement is the odd one out and why.

Why it's effective

When children work to identify what is the odd one out, they will be conjecturing and reasoning about the items in the set. Almost without realising it, they will create their own generalisations, and test all parts of the set given to them against this to try and identify the 'odd one out'.

Tips for use

This strategy works particularly well when time for paired or grouped discussion is given, with children attempting to convince each other as to which item from the set is the odd one out.

To further increase the reasoning required, especially when children have had some experience responding to this strategy, always aim to choose the set of numbers/statements you provide so that there is more than one possible 'answer.' This can create a good debate in the classroom, with different children trying to convince each other that the number they have selected is the 'real' odd one out.

This strategy could also be combined with the 'Another, another, another' strategy, by asking children to generate further examples that would either be similar to the 'odd one out' or to the rest of the set.

Watch out

⚠ **Children may not see the link between parts of the set.**

Sometimes the children will struggle to find the odd one out as they cannot spot the generalities (links) between different parts of the set. Focusing children's thinking using the 'What's the same? What's different?' key strategy, initially with pairs from the set, can help children see the similarities and differences between parts of the set. Using 'panic envelopes' (see page 11) containing key questions to focus thinking can also be effective in supporting children to see the link between parts of the set.

Try these

Below are some examples to introduce your class to this strategy. In these examples, the content level is sometimes lower than that set out in the National Curriculum for Year 4. This is to allow children to focus on the development of reasoning skills, without being restricted by subject knowledge.

Look at this set of numbers: 30, 20, 36, 3. Which is the odd one out?
Possible 'odd one outs' with reasons and key questions/follow-ups:
➤ 3: the only odd number
➤ 20: the only number that is not a multiple of 3
   Which times tables do these numbers appear in? Do any of the numbers have a common multiple?
➤ 36: the only number with an odd number of factors
   What can we call these numbers??
   If you arranged 9 counters into an array, what shape would you make?

 **Case studies from the classroom**

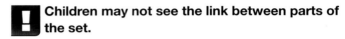 A snippet from a conversation between two Year 4 children discussing the question: *Look at 6 × 10 = ?, 0.6 × 10 = ? or 60 × 10 = ? Which is the odd one out?*

Look at these calculations: 6 × 10 = ?, 0.6 × 10 = ?, 60 × 10 = ? Which is the odd one out?

Possible 'odd one outs' with reasons and key questions/follow ups:

➤ 0.6 × 10: only calculation with a decimal
  Follow this up with discussion about why this is and the role of 0 as a place holder.
➤ 0.6 × 10: only calculation which gives a single-digit answer

Look at these shapes: Which is the odd one out?

Possible 'odd one outs' with reasons and key questions/follow-ups:

➤ Equilateral triangle: only shape that is not a rectangle/only shape where the total of interior angles is 180 degrees
  What are the interior angles of each shape?
  What do we call a shape where there are four interior angles which are each 90 degrees?
➤ Equilateral triangle: only shape with three sides
➤ Oblong: only shape that is not regular
  What do you notice about the side lengths in each shape?
  What do you call a shape where all sides are the same length?

Look at these fractions: $\frac{6}{8}, \frac{12}{16}, \frac{3}{4}, \frac{66}{88}, \frac{33}{44}, \frac{51}{68}, \frac{8}{10}$. Which is the odd one out?

Possible 'odd one outs' with reasons and key questions/follow-ups:

➤ $\frac{8}{10}$: only fraction that is not equivalent to $\frac{3}{4}$
  How do you know it is not equivalent to $\frac{3}{4}$?
➤ $\frac{33}{44}$: only fraction where the numerator and denominator are both multiples of 11
  Does this help you write this fraction in another way?

 Activities and investigations

Child A: 6 is the odd one out, because it is the only number without a zero.

Child B: But, is 0.6 × 10 the odd one out? Because it is the only one that doesn't have a zero in the answer, it isn't a 10 or a 100. It is also the odd one out because it is the only one to have zero before you times it.

8 Peculiar, obvious, general

💡 Key strategy

Ask the children to give a peculiar, obvious, and if they are able, general, example of a statement.

Why it's effective

This key strategy encourages children to think about the structure of mathematics and the definition of the statements given. Through focusing on what makes a peculiar, obvious or general example of a given statement children have to think carefully about the statement given, the criteria needed to meet the statement, and what examples they could give. The encouragement to give a peculiar example encourages children to push the boundaries of their understanding, whilst the general example encourages children to begin to develop algebraic thinking.

Tips for use

This key strategy could be used either as part of shared learning, as the main activity in the lesson or as an effective plenary. The children should be encouraged to explain their choices, either verbally or in writing, which will encourage them to think about the definition of the given statement and the general structure of mathematics. The strategy works particularly well if they are encouraged to discuss and convince each other that their examples fit with the statement and are peculiar, obvious or general. When working in pairs, they can also be encouraged to think of reasons why their partner's responses may not be peculiar, obvious or general.

Encourage children to first state record an **obvious** example. *What is the first example you think of? Why is this the first example that you think of?* They can always replace their obvious example with a 'more obvious' example whilst they are thinking through the activity.

Then ask children to think of their **peculiar** example. Encourage them to think about the definition and criteria of the statement given. *What fits our definition, but isn't obvious?*

Finally, children should be encouraged to think about a **general** example. This will deepen their thinking about the statement given and their understanding.

Depending on the desired outcomes and ability of the children to reason, the requirement for a general example could be skipped.

Watch out for

Children may rush for a really big or small number.

In numerical questions, children will often state a really large or small number, which they arrive at by multiplying or dividing by 10, 100, 1000, etc. as their peculiar example. Discuss with the children if, just because an example is really large or small, it is peculiar. *What makes it peculiar? Is it really quite obvious as all we have done is multiplied/divided by a large number?* You can also modify the question to remove the temptation to go really large, e.g. *Can you give me a peculiar example of an odd number that is below 70?*

Children's general statements may not be general.

Using the strategy 'Always, sometimes, never' to encourage children to check their general statements can help children ensure their statements are truly general.

Case studies from the classroom

A snippet from a conversation between two Year 4 children discussing the question: *Give me a peculiar, obvious and general example of a multiple of 9.*

Try these

The examples below were given by children who trialled this resource. Example follow-up questions are provided where appropriate.

Give me a peculiar, obvious and general example of a quadrilateral.

➤ Peculiar: *Why is a square a quadrilateral?*

➤ Obvious: *Why is this an obvious quadrilateral? How can you be sure it is a quadrilateral?*

➤ General: A shape with four sides. *What is the general term for a shape with straight sides?*

Give me a peculiar, obvious and general example of a multiple of 6.

Give me a peculiar, obvious and general example of numbers with a product of 280.
➤ Peculiar: *17.5 × 16 as it involves a decimal (but you can prove it gives a product of 280 by repeated halving).*
➤ Obvious: *280 × 1 as it's clear it has a product of 280.*
➤ General: *Any numbers which multiply together to make 280.*

Give me a peculiar, obvious and general example of a number which rounds to 1100.

Give me a peculiar, obvious and general example of a shape with a perimeter of 12 units.

Give me a peculiar, obvious and general example of a fraction bigger than 1.

Give me a peculiar, obvious and general example of a fraction.

Give me a peculiar, obvious and general example of a shape with two lines of symmetry.

Give me a peculiar, obvious and general example of a way of presenting data.

 Activities and investigations

1 Make 100
2 A bit of magic
5 Moving and shaping
7 Tricky tangrams
12 Mystery numbers
14 Symmetry squared
15 Terrific thirty-six

Child A: 9 is obvious, as it's the first multiple!

Child B: A peculiar one would be one where it's not immediately obvious it's a multiple of 9, like 504.

Child A: General would be any number which divides by 9 without leaving a remainder.

Silly answers

Key strategy

Ask the children to give you a 'silly' answer to a question and explain why it is a silly answer.

Why it's effective

By asking children to give you a 'silly' answer to a question they will have to reason about the range which the possible 'correct' answers could fall into. This will require them to consider the properties that the question entails, and will involve them in making a generalisation about the 'correct' answer(s) in order to explain why their answer is silly.

Tips for use

Always ensure you ask the the children to justify their silly answer and explain why it can't possibly be a 'correct' answer.

The children can also be asked to create a number of 'silly' answers and then to order them in order of 'silliness'. Encourage them to identify which 'silly' answer is close to the 'real' answer or involves a common error/misconception. This can be a great way to address misconceptions with them.

Modifiers can also be added to the base question to restrict the range of possible silly answers. Depending on the restrictions added, this can prompt deeper thinking and reasoning.

This strategy works well when children are given the opportunity to discuss their 'silly' answer(s) and reasons why they are 'silly'. The strategy 'What's the same? What's different?' can be used to encourage children to compare, contrast and look for links between their 'silly' answers.

Watch out

 Children may always give very large answers.

Children's natural instinct when asked for a 'silly' answer often is to go for a very large answer (e.g. *4 trillion, infinity, etc.*). Depending on the question given, either ask children if they can prove that this is not an answer to the question (particularly interesting when the question relates to a statement, rather than a calculation) or place a restriction on the range of answers allowed.

Try these

Below are some examples to introduce your class to this strategy. In these examples, the content level is sometimes lower than that set out in the National Curriculum for Year 4. This is to allow children to focus on the development of reasoning skills, without being restricted by subject knowledge.

Give me a silly answer for a factor of 22.
Prompt questions:
➤ *What is a factor?*
➤ *What do we know about the numbers which are factors of any given number?*

Example silly answers and justification:
➤ **23**: this is higher than 22 and factors are whole numbers which multiply together to make a number, therefore the factor of a number cannot be higher than the number itself
➤ **0.5**: this is a decimal number and factors always have to be integers

 **Case studies from the classroom**

A snippet from a conversation between two Year 4 children discussing the question: *Give me a silly answer for 196.*

Give me a silly answer for 4123 – ? = 3232
Prompt questions:
➤ *How would we work out the missing number?*

Example silly answers and justification:
➤ **1000**: that would make 3123, as it's simple to take 1000 away from a number
➤ **1102**: it's higher than 1000. We know that 412 – 1000 = 3123, therefore the missing number must be less than 1000.
➤ **832:** the last digit is not 1. We know it must be, as the difference between the last digits in the two numbers we know is 1.

Give me a silly answer for another way of expressing 8 × 7 = 56
Prompt questions:
➤ *How else could you express the number? Explore commutatively and the distributive law.*

Example silly answers and justification:
➤ **8 × 2 + 8 × 4:** 2 + 4 do not add up to 7, therefore it is not a correct use of the distributive law

Give me a silly answer for a drawing of a quadrilateral.
Example silly answers and justification:

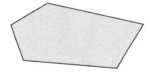

➤ because it has more than four sides

➤ because it has less than four sides

Give me a silly answer for an equivalent fraction to $\frac{6}{7}$.
Example silly answers and justification:
➤ $\frac{4}{7}$: it has the same denominator as $\frac{6}{7}$
➤ $\frac{4}{14}$: 14 is not a multiple of 4, and 4 is not a multiple of 3

Give me a silly answer for the question if the answer is 196.
Example silly answers and justification:
➤ **196 – 11**: as you are taking away a positive number from your target answer, which will always result in a smaller number
➤ **19 × 10:** you are multiplying by 10, so you are making your starting number 10 times bigger, which would be 190, not 196

Child A: 196 – 100 would be silly because the answer is 196 and you're taking away more so it can't be the answer so the answer will be smaller.

Child B: 200 – 196, because you're taking away the answer from a number just a bit bigger so it will be a much lower number than 196.

What do you notice?

 ## Key strategy

Ask the children 'What do you notice?' about a number, set of numbers, shape or mathematical statement.

Why it's effective

This strategy encourages children to look deeper at the structure of mathematics. Through answering the question 'What do you notice?' children will be making their own generalisations and testing them against specific examples.

Tips for use

This strategy is very effective when the children are given time to talk and discuss the statement with a partner or small groups, before feeding back to the class (larger group) with the expectation that they convince the larger group of what they notice.

When using this strategy, you can provide children with sets of numbers/mathematical objects (e.g. *7, 14, 21, 28; a rectangle, a square and rhombus*) or general statements/properties (e.g. *all multiples of 3, what happens when you multiply by 100?*).

The children's reasoning skills can be further developed by asking follow-up questions or providing follow-up statements once they have responded to the initial 'What do you notice?' question. The strategy 'Always, sometimes, never' true often works well as a follow up to a 'What do you notice?' question as this allows children to further develop their generalisations.

This strategy can also be used alongside many of the other key strategies, which can help to focus children's thinking and reasoning.

Watch out

Children may not see the generalities.

Sometimes children will be unable to independently state the generality or generalities relating to the statement which has been given. To help children see the generality, use follow-up questions, which could involve some of the other key strategies. 'What's the same? What's different?' is particularly effective here. Panic envelopes, with follow-up questions (see page 11) can also be used.

Try these

Below are some examples to introduce your class to this strategy. In these examples, the content level is sometimes lower than that set out in the National Curriculum for Year 4. This is to allow children to focus on the development of reasoning skills, without being restricted by subject knowledge.

What do you notice about multiples of odd numbers?
➤ *Can you list some multiples of 4? Of 8? Of 16?*
➤ *What's the same, what's different about these multiples?* (all even numbers)
➤ *Why is this the case?*
➤ *What is another way of thinking about multiplication?* (repeated addition)
➤ *What happens when you add an even number to an even number?* (You always get an even number.)

Case studies from the classroom

A snippet from a conversation between two Year 4 children discussing the question: *What do you notice about multiples of 25?*

What do you notice about multiples of 25?

➤ *Can you list some multiples of 25?*
➤ *What's the same? What's different about these multiples?*
➤ *How can you tell if a number is a multiple of 25?*
➤ *What numbers are all multiples of 25 also multiples of? How do you know?*

What do you notice about multiples of 9?

➤ *Can you list some multiples of 9?*
➤ *What's the same? What's different about these multiples?*
➤ *Find the digit sum of each of your multiples of 9. What do you notice?* (digit sum (adding the digits in the number together, e.g. *digit sum of 27 is 2 + 7 = 9*) is also 9)
➤ *Can you use this knowledge to say if any number is a multiple of 9? Is 426 a multiple of 9? How about 1107? How do you know?*

What do you notice about fraction and decimal equivalents for hundredths and tenths?

➤ *Can you list some decimals that are equivalent to fractions with a denominator of 100 or 10?*
➤ *What's the same? What's different about these equivalents?*
➤ *How could you convert any decimal number into a fraction with a denominator of 10 or 100?*

What do you notice about this set of numbers: 9, 18, 27, 36?

➤ *What would the next number be in this sequence?*

What do you notice about the lines of symmetry in a rectangle?

➤ *Let's draw some rectangles. How many lines of symmetry do they have?*
➤ *Do all the rectangles have the same lines of symmetry?*
➤ *Is this the same for all quadrilaterals?*

What do you notice about fractions which are equivalent to $\frac{3}{4}$?

➤ *Let's list some equivalent fractions to $\frac{3}{4}$.*
➤ *What do you notice about the numerators and denominators in these fractions?*
➤ *Can you give me a peculiar, obvious and general equivalent fraction to $\frac{3}{4}$?*

What do you notice about what happens when you multiply by 100?

➤ *What appears to happen when you multiply 45 by 100?*
➤ *Does the same happen if you multiply 0.45 by 100?*

What do you notice about the perimeter of an equilateral triangle?

➤ *Let's draw some equilateral triangles. Let's measure the perimeters.*
➤ *What do you notice/what do you know about side lengths of rectangles?*
➤ *What are the lengths of each side of these rectangles?*
➤ *Is there any link between the lengths of the sides and the perimeter of the triangle?*
➤ *Can you use this to give a general statement (formula) to find the perimeter of a rectangle?*

Activities and investigations

1 Make 100
9 Finding the difference
10 Highest and lowest
11 Disco drinks
13 Crack the code
14 Symmetry squared
17 Fraction strips

Child A: The units go up in a pattern: 5, 0, 5, 0, 5, 0.

Child B: Yes, and the last two digits are always 25, 50, 75 or 00.

Child A: Yes, the tens and units repeat when they get to any new hundred.

Key strategy

Give the children an 'If ... ' statement (e.g. $\frac{1}{2}$ *of 80 is 40*), and ask them what else they know based on this statement.

Why it's effective

This strategy encourages children to see the links that exist in all areas of mathematics. It encourages them to reason and combine other known facts with the statement. This activity works particularly well as a starter or plenary, or as an early morning challenge.

Tips for use

Provide the statement and the allow children to record everything else they know. Adding a time and/or quantity challenge, (e.g. *Can you state at least ten other facts in two minutes?*) can help to add an element of competition!

Try asking the whole class to work on a statement individually, then to share their related facts with a partner, then ask each pair to share with the class a related fact that they think that no one else would have come up with. This approach pushes children to think deeper and go beyond the 'obvious' related facts. A mind map can be a useful tool for recording responses to this strategy, with children recording groups of related facts on each arm of their mind maps.

You can also work with children on the 'automatic' related facts that they should be able to state almost instantaneously, e.g. inverse facts (e.g. *7 × 8 = 8 × 7*) and multiples of 10, (e.g. *70 × 8, 7 × 80, etc.*).

The strategy can also be used with 'real-life' statements, e.g. *if we know that $\frac{1}{8}$ of a class are boys and there are 32 in the class, what else do we know?* (See exemplification below.)

The 'Peculiar, obvious, general' strategy can also be used alongside 'What else do we know?' to deepen the thinking from this strategy.

Watch out

Children may 'stall'.

Sometimes children will come up with a few 'obvious' related facts (perhaps using inverses, etc), but then struggle to see any other related facts. Asking children to discuss ideas together can help overcome this, as can encouraging children to 'combine' related facts, e.g. *use an inverse and also divide by 10 (so 0.4 × 5 = 2 is related to 5 × 4 = 20)*.

Facts/statements may not be related.

Sometimes children will provide facts/statements that appear to have no clear relation to the given statement, but be careful not to say categorically that it is not a related fact. Instead, encourage children to explain how it is related, talking you, or another child through the steps they have taken to form this related fact. Analysing untrue 'facts' given by children can also help expose any misconceptions that they may hold.

Try these

Below are some examples to introduce your class to this strategy. In these examples, the content level is sometimes lower than that set out in the National Curriculum for Year 4. This is to allow children to focus on the development of reasoning skills, without being restricted by subject knowledge.

Case studies from the classroom

A snippet from a conversation between two Year 4 children discussing the question: *If we know that know that $\frac{1}{4} = \frac{2}{8}$, what else do we know?*

If we know that 8 × 7 = 56, what else do we know?
- ➤ 7 × 8 = 56, 70 × 8 = 560, 8 × 70 = 560 *How about 80 × 70, is that 560 too? Why?/Why not?* (80 × 70 = 5600)
- ➤ 56 ÷ 7 = 8, 56 ÷ 8 = 7 *Can we use our multiples of 10 and 1000 to create other facts?*
- ➤ 560 ÷ 70 = 80, 560 ÷ 80 = 7, 560 ÷ 8 = 70 *How about dividing by 10 or 100?*
- ➤ *How about using our doubling and halving skills?* 7 × 4 = 28, 7 × 16 = 112
- ➤ This could then be extended further, e.g. using inverse and place value with these double and halved statements, multiply by 4 and 8, etc.

If we know that $\frac{3}{4} = \frac{9}{12}$, what else do we know?
- ➤ *How are these fractions linked?*
- ➤ *Can you prove using a diagram that these are equivalent?*
- ➤ *How else could we generate other equivalent fractions?*

If we know that one side of a pentagon is 7 cm long, what else do we know?
- ➤ *What is special about the length of all sides in a square?*

➤ *How do you find the perimeter of a square?*

If we know that 3400 + 3200 = 6600, what else do we know?

If we know that $\frac{5}{100}$ = 0.05, what else do we know?

If we know that 1000 m = 1 km what else do we know?

If we know that an even number plus an odd number always equals an odd number, what else do we know?

 Activities and investigations

Child A: I know that $\frac{1}{4}$ also equals $\frac{2}{8}$.

Child B: I think you can times the top and bottom of the fraction by the same number and it'll still be equal.

Child A: Yes, I think that's right, so we know that $\frac{5}{20}$ and $\frac{8}{32} = \frac{1}{4}$.

12 What's the same? What's different?

Key strategy

Give the children at least two statements, objects or numbers and ask them to compare them by asking, 'What's the same? What's different?'

Why it's effective

This strategy encourages children to compare and contrast. It fosters their ability to spot patterns and similarities, to make generalisations and to spot connections between different aspects of mathematics. The open-ended nature of the key strategy enables all children to contribute, regardless of their ability and support can easily be added.

Tips for use

Introduce the two (or more) things that you want the children to compare and simply ask 'What's the same? What's different?' This can work well individually, or through paired or grouped discussion. You could ask children to write their ideas on sticky notes, and share these together as a class, discussing each statement as it is shared.

The strategy can be used with two things, but can also be effective when used with more, as this can help develop the children's ability to spot relationships. The strategy can also be used effectively alongside the 'Odd one out' strategy.

Key prompt questions can also be provided to groups who may need more support, or more generally when you need to scaffold children's thinking in a particular direction. These could be provided on 'panic sheets' (see Problem-solving techniques on page 11) which children should use only if they cannot think of anything that is the same/different themselves.

Watch out

Children may point out 'superficial' similarities/differences (e.g. they are both numbers).

These should not be discouraged and the more often the children are exposed to this strategy, the more 'mathematical' their responses will become. Providing prompt questions or panic sheets as described above can help the children focus their thinking and produce deeper similarities/differences, which demonstrates a greater level of reasoning.

Try these

Below are some examples to introduce your class to this strategy. In these examples, the content level is sometimes lower than that set out in the National Curriculum for Year 4. This is to allow children to focus on the development of reasoning skills, without being restricted by subject knowledge.

What's the same and what's different about 9 and 81?
➤ Same: both multiples of 9/in the 9 times table, both have a digit sum (when you add up all the digits in the number) of 9, both a multiple of 3, both are greater than 8
➤ Different: 81 is a 2-digit number, 9 is a 1-digit number, 9 is not a multiple of 27 or 81
➤ Draw attention to the fact that both numbers have an odd number of factors and are square numbers. You could show this by representing both as an array (3 × 3, 9 × 9). Discuss how we know that if 9 is a multiple of 3 that 81 must also be a multiple of 3.

Case studies from the classroom

A snippet from a conversation between two Year 4 children discussing the question: *What's the same and what's different about a cube and a cuboid?*

What's the same and what's different about 2500 and 4000?

➤ Same: both multiples of 25, both multiples of 100, both multiples of 50, both 4-digit numbers, both above 2000

➤ Different: 4000 is a multiple of 1000, 4000 is bigger than 2500

➤ Draw attention to how you can identify multiples of 25 and 1000.

What's the same and what's different about $\frac{2}{5}$ and $\frac{4}{10}$?

➤ Same: both fractions, both a proportion, both numerators are multiples of 2, both denominators are multiples of 5, both are equivalent to $\frac{2}{5}$

➤ Different: the numerator and denominators are not the same

➤ Draw attention to how the numerators are linked by a common multiple and the denominators are also linked by a common multiple, leading into how this can be used to identify equivalent fractions.

What's the same and what's different about a cube and a cuboid?

➤ Same: both 3-D shapes, both have rectangle faces, both have six faces

➤ Different: cube made up of square faces

What's the same and what's different about a pictogram and bar chart?

➤ Same: both show data, both are types of graphs

➤ Different: pictograms have items repressing value, bar charts do not

➤ Explore the different types of data possible to display on different types of graphs/charts.

 Activities and investigations

Child A: They both have 8 corners, and 12 vertices.

Child B: I think vertices are corners! They have 8 vertices and 12 sides.

Child A: Yes, you're right! They also both have 6 faces.

Zooming in

Key strategy

Ask the children to give you an example that fits with a given criteria, (e.g. *an even number*) and then 'zoom in' to give further criteria which their number has to fit, (e.g. *an odd number which is also a multiple of 7*).

Why it's effective

This strategy encourages children to reason about mathematical properties and gets them re-evaluating the properties of their initial 'answer' to check it meets the additional criteria as it is revealed. The children will soon begin to try and anticipate how you may 'zoom in' to narrow down the criteria and make more reasoned choices for their initial 'answers'.

Tips for use

The key strategy is particularly effective when launching a new topic or focus area, as it can allow children to demonstrate their current knowledge, as well as encouraging them to explore the boundaries of their current understanding. The strategy is also particularly effective as a plenary or at the end of a topic in order to assess understanding.

The children should normally be allowed to change their answer if it does not fit the new criteria revealed, however you may want to reward children whose initial answer still met all criteria.

You can, however, make the game competitive by saying that a child is 'out' if their number no longer fits. Keep revealing criteria until there is only one possible answer or there is only one child left. This encourages more sophisticated thinking as the children try to anticipate what further criteria you will add to 'zoom in'.

Once you have revealed all of your criteria you can promote further reasoning and mathematical discussion by asking the children if they can think of any other answers that would meet all of the 'zoomed in' criteria. This activity can also be combined with the 'Peculiar, obvious, general' strategy. *Can you give a peculiar answer that would fit all the 'zoomed in' criteria?*

You can also use grids of numbers/images from which the children select based on the criteria given. (An example grid is provided on the CD-ROM which you can adapt as desired.) Depending on the content of your grid, this can either provide support for less able children, or can provide extra challenge by restricting the possible choices when 'zooming in'.

Finally, the children can also be asked to create their own set of 'Zooming in' criteria, which encourages them to think in more depth about properties of number/shape.

Watch out

! **Children may struggle to test their answers with further statements.**

Ensure that children have a secure understanding of the terminology used in the statements given. Working as pairs or in small groups on this activity can also help with this by providing a source of peer support. It may also be that the pace at which you are adding the further statements is too demanding for some children.

Case studies from the classroom

Teacher: Give me a multiple of 25.

Child: 25

Try these

Below are some examples to introduce your class to this strategy. In these examples, the content level is sometimes lower than that set out in the National Curriculum for Year 4. This is to allow children to focus on the development of reasoning skills, without being restricted by subject knowledge.

Give me a fraction greater than 0.5.
➤ *Zoom in so the numerator (the top number in the fraction) is even.*
➤ *Zoom in so the denominator (the bottom number in the fraction) is greater than 3.*

Give me a multiple of 25.
➤ *Zoom in so the number is greater than 250.*
➤ *Zoom in so that it is also a multiple of 50.*

Give me a decimal number.
➤ *Zoom in so the number is less than 0.5.*
➤ *Zoom in so that the number is equal to $\frac{46}{100}$.*

Give me a decimal time.
➤ *Zoom in so it is a time written in the 24-hour clock.*
➤ *Zoom in so that is after 7 o'clock in the evening.*
➤ *Zoom in so that it is before quarter to 8 in the evening.*

Draw me a quadrilateral.
➤ *Zoom in so it has only one set of parallel lines.*
➤ *Zoom in so the shape is irregular.*

Draw me a peculiar triangle.
➤ *Zoom in so that it has an angle greater than 90 degrees.*
➤ *Zoom in so that it is not an isosceles triangle.*
Discuss that a triangle with an angle over 90 degrees and not isosceles must make it a scalene triangle.

Give me a number under 10.
➤ *Zoom in so that the number is a negative number.*
➤ *Zoom in so that it is greater than ⁻10.*

Give me/point to a number over 10.
(This example could be completed using the grid provided on the CD-ROM.)

48	11	8	44
63	36	12	58
20	47	40	24
17	4	113	28
56	187	440	16

➤ *Zoom in so that it is an odd number.*
➤ *Zoom in so that the number's digit sum is over 10. (The digit sum is the total of the digits in the number, e.g. 4 + 9 for 49.)*
➤ *Zoom in so that is has only two factors.*
47 is the more obvious example from the grid, but can children find another example that also fits all criteria? (113)

Give me/point to a multiple of 4.
(This example could be completed using the grid provided on the CD-ROM.)
➤ *Zoom in so that the number is under 40.*
➤ *Zoom in so that it is also a multiple of 8.*
➤ *Zoom in so that it is not a multiple of 12.*
Only 24 fits all criteria. Ask, *If we zoomed out so the number didn't have to be under 40, would there be any other possible answers?*

Teacher: That is bigger than 300.

Child: 325

Teacher: That is less than 380.

Child: 375

Key strategy

In addition to the key strategies outlined, the following question structures can also help embed problem-solving and reasoning into day-to-day maths teaching.

Can you give me an example of ... ?
➤ *a multiple of 25*
➤ *an irregular shape*
➤ *two fractions that are equivalent*

What is the quickest or easiest way to ... ?
➤ *multiply TU × TU (e.g. 34 × 35)*
➤ *find out the factors of a number*
➤ *find the perimeter of a rectangle*
➤ *find out how many tables will fit into our school hall*

What is/are ... an example of?
➤ *3, 5, 7 (numbers with only two factors)*
➤ *isosceles, scalene, equilateral (types of triangle)*
➤ *22 cm² (an area)*

How can we be sure that ... ?
➤ *all multiples of 4 are multiples of 2*
➤ *multiples of 25 are also multiples of 5*
➤ *$\frac{3}{4}$ is equal to $\frac{6}{8}$*

Is ... a good explanation of ... ?
➤ *part of a whole ... a fraction*
➤ *a number that ends in an even number ... multiples of 4*
➤ *adding a 0 on the end of the number ... multiplying by 10 (No, consider what happens when you multiply 0.7 × 10.)*

What's the link between ... ?
➤ *3, 5, 7, and 11*
➤ *$\frac{3}{4}, \frac{6}{8}, \frac{9}{18}$*
➤ *an oblong and square*

Activities and investigations

1 Make 100!

Learning objective	Reasoning skills	Curriculum link
• To solve problems by using properties of numbers.	• Working systematically • Finding all possibilities • Conjecturing and convincing	**1,3** Number and place value: multiples

The problem

Make 100!

This activity is all about trying to make 100, just using the numbers 5 and 10 and the operation of addition.

You could make lots of different numbers, including 100. For example, you could make 100 by adding:
$10 + 10 + 10 + 10 + 10 + 10 + 10 + 10$ (or 8×10) and
$5 + 5 + 5 + 5$ (or 4×5).

You could also make 100 by using (4×10) and (5×12) along with many other combinations.

What other pairs of numbers could you use to add together to make 100? For example, could you make 100 only using the numbers 2 and 3? How about 7 and 9? How about 4 and 7?

Your challenge

Investigate which pairs of numbers you could combine to make 100.
Are there any pairs of numbers that won't work?

Things to think about:

- Are there any numbers that you immediately know could combine to make 100? What makes you know that these pairs will work straightaway?
- Do smaller value number pairs have more or less possible solutions than larger value number pairs? Why?
- Does it matter if you have an even/odd, even/even or odd/odd pairing?
- Can you use your knowledge of multiples of numbers to work out if a pair of numbers could combine to make 100?

RISING STARS
Maths

Year 4 · Problem Solving and Reasoning

Background knowledge

- Children are asked to investigate which pairs of numbers can be combined to make 100.
- For example, the numbers 3 and 5 can be combined to make 100 e.g. $(3 \times 5) + (5 \times 17)$.
- In order to solve this problem, children will need to be able to list multiples of each number 1–9.
- Multiples are formed by multiplying the number you are finding multiples of by a whole number.
- If children list the multiples of two numbers until they reach 100, they can then look for pairs of numbers that combine to make 100.

- For example, if investigating the digits 6 and 7:
  - multiples of 6: 6, 12, 18, 24, 30, 36, 42, 48, 54, 60, 66, 72, 78, 84, 90, 96
  - multiples of 7: 7, 14, 21, 28, 35, 42, 49, 56, 63, 70, 77, 84, 91, 98

  You can then see that 30 (6×5) and 70 (7×10) both combine to make 100, as do 28 (7×4) and 72 (6×12).
- Children could then work out all possible combinations of numbers 2–10 by listing the multiples of 2–9 and looking for combinations that total 100.

Launching the activity

1. Begin by reviewing counting in multiples, then show the prompt poster. Give children time to discuss with a partner the prompt and their initial ideas and ways which they could tackle the problem.

1. Discuss these initial ideas together, recording any conjectures made by the children on the board and/or working wall.

2. Ask which maths facts they may need to know to help them solve the problem. Establish that the knowledge of multiples of each number may be useful.

3. Working in pairs, one child should list all the multiples of 5 while their partner should list all the multiples of 10 until they go over 100. Ask them to see if they can spot how the combinations stated in the poster have been found. Can they find any other combinations of the numbers 5 and 10 which combine to make 100?

4. Provide time for children to work in pairs or small groups on the main problem, investigating which pairs of numbers can total 100, and, importantly, if there are any pairs of numbers between 1–10 which cannot be combined to make 100. Graffiti maths can work particularly well for this problem.

5. Towards the end of the session bring the class back together and discuss their findings and anything they have noticed.

Developing reasoning

➤ **What do you notice** about the multiples of ... / about the numbers which combine to make 100?
➤ Give me a **hard and easy** pair of numbers to prove that they total 100.
➤ Give me a **peculiar, obvious and general** pair of numbers that can be combined to total 100.

➤ Can you give me a way of using these two numbers to make 100? A**nother, another, another.**
➤ **Convince me** that these numbers do/do not combine to make 100.
➤ If we know that these two numbers combine to make 100, **what else do we know?**

Providing differentiation

Support
Children will benefit from using a multiplication square to support their identification of multiples. Practical representations such as counters, cubes or number rods may also help to enable children to represent the combination of groups of each number.

Extension
Children could explore a wider range of numbers, for example, exploring combinations of numbers between 1–20.

 Key strategies

4   Hard and easy
8   Peculiar, obvious, general
10 What do you notice?
11 What else do we know?
12 What's the same? What's different?

 Problem-solving approaches

Group work; Graffiti maths

Taking it further

Children could be extended to explore further patterns with multiples of numbers, e.g. combinations of three multiples to make 100.

Learning objective	Reasoning skills	Curriculum link
• To solve problems by identifying patterns and relationships between numbers.	• Making generalisations • Conjecturing and convincing	**1-3** Number and place value: identify patterns

The problem

Problem 2

A bit of magic

Have a look at this square which is filled with the numbers 1, 2 and 3.

We say this is a 'magic square'. The numbers in all of the rows, columns and diagonals add up to the same total (in this case 6: 1 + 2 + 3 = 6).

1	3	2
3	2	1
2	1	3

Is it possible to create a 3 × 3 magic square using the numbers 1–9?

Things to think about:

• Is there anything special about the total of the numbers in the square and the magic number?

• If you can work out the magic number before creating the magic square?

Your challenge

Investigate magic squares and create some others.
Can you create a 3 × 3 magic square using the numbers 4, 5 and 6?
How about using non-consecutive numbers?
Can you complete the ultimate challenge of making a 3 × 3 square using the numbers 1 to 9?

RISING STARS
Maths

Year 4

Problem Solving and Reasoning

Background knowledge

• This problem revolves around the classic magic square problem.

• Magic squares are squares in which the numbers in the rows, columns and diagonals all total to the same 'magic number'. Magic squares can vary in size from a simple 2 × 2 square to much larger ones.

• In a 3 × 3 magic square, the magic number is always equal to 3× the number at the centre of the square. This is found by adding all the numbers in the square and dividing by 3 (as the total is shared between 3 columns/rows, etc.).

• Related magic squares using consecutive numbers can be created based on the example provided in the poster problem. E.g. in a magic square using the

4	6	5
6	5	4
5	4	6

values 4, 5, 6, we have substituted the value 1 for 4, 2 for 5 and 3 for 6.

• For magic squares which use just three different consecutive numbers, each number must be present in each row, column and diagonal.

• Once the children have identified how to find the magic number, solving magic squares becomes considerably simpler. For example, in a magic square made up of the numbers 8, 10, 12, the magic number would need to be 30.

8	12	10
12	10	8
10	8	12

• Children can therefore work out that the magic number for a 1–9 square must be 15 (1 + 2 + 3 + 4 + 5 + 6 + 7 + 8 + 9 = 45, 45 divided by 3 = 15).

8	3	4
1	5	9
6	7	2

• Through trial and improvement they can then solve the 1–9 magic square.

Launching the activity

1. Begin by showing the magic square from the prompt poster. Give children two minutes to discuss with a partner, *What do you notice?*

2. Discuss what they think about the square together, drawing attention to the fact that the rows, columns and diagonals all total the same value. Record any other relationships the children note.

3. Introduce the challenge from the poster.

4. Discuss together how the challenged could be attempted and then set children off, working in small groups to create other magic squares. Graffiti maths is an effective technique for this problem.

5. Through discussion and questioning during independent work, draw attention to the relationship between the magic number and the total of the digits in the square.

6. Encourage children to use this relationship to help them create other magic squares, and to ultimately solve the 1–9 magic square.

7. At the end of the session, draw children back together and ask, *What did you notice?*, sharing their findings from the session.

Developing reasoning

➤ *What do you notice* about the magic square/ the magic number/the total of the numbers in the magic square?

➤ Give me a *hard and easy* magic square. What makes it hard/easy?

➤ *Convince me* that this square is magic.

➤ Give me a *peculiar, obvious and general* magic square.

➤ If we know the digits that are in the square *what else do we know?*

Providing differentiation

Support
Further examples of magic squares could be provided for the children. They could also be supported in creating magic squares by first representing the square using counters/cubes or other physical representations.

Extension
The children could explore how one magic square could be used to create related squares, for example, by adding 3 to each digit in the 1–9 magic square, a new (but related) magic square is created. They could also be challenged to investigate which sets of three digits will create a magic square and which sets cannot create one.

 Key strategies

4   Hard and easy
8   Peculiar, obvious, general
10 What do you notice?
11 What else do we know?

 Problem-solving approaches

Group work; Graffiti maths

Taking it further

The children could be extended to explore different sized magic squares, e.g. could they create a magic 4 × 4 square?

3 | What's my number?

Learning objective
- To understand place value in numbers with up to four digits.

Reasoning skills
- Spotting patterns
- Working systematically
- Solving problems

Curriculum link
1.3 Number and place value: place value in up to four digits

The problem

Problem 3

What's my number?

Here's a game of 'guess who' with a maths twist!

With a partner, you each have a copy of the same guess who board and a pencil.

Each choose a number from your board and write it in your 'my number' box.

Then, in turn, ask your partner a question to try and work out the number they have written. You could ask for example, *Does your number have an 8 in the tenths place?* or *Is your number bigger than 2?*

Your partner must answer 'yes' or 'no'.

Use their answer to work out which numbers they can't have chosen and cross these off your board.

Continue until one of you has worked out your partner's chosen number.

Things to think about:

- Does it matter which number you choose as your number?
- Is there any number that you should never choose as your number? Why?
- What questions can you ask that allow you to cross off the most numbers and get closer to your partner's chosen number?
- Can you ask any questions that do not involve place value, e.g. that do not take the form 'does your number have *x* in the *y* place?

Your challenge

Play the game thinking about what strategies you can use to help you win!

RISING STARS
Maths

Year 4 | Problem Solving and Reasoning

Background knowledge

- This investigation is based on the game 'guess who' where the children have to ask questions to identify the number that their partner has selected from their game board.
- Each place in a number is named as follows:
  - TThThHTU.th
  - Ten Thousands Thousands Hundreds Tens Unit. tenths hundredths
- Four versions of the game board are provided. Board 1 includes ThHTU numbers. Board 2 includes TThThHTU numbers. Board 3 includes numbers with up to two decimal places and Board 4 includes HTU numbers and is intended for children who don't yet have a secure knowledge of place value.

- All grids contain a range of numbers which require careful questioning to differentiate between. However, on each grid there is at least one number which, if chosen, could be indentified with a single question.
- Numbers lines, both marked and empty, are an effective resource to help children understand place value. Gattegno charts (place value charts) can also be used effectively.

Launching the activity

1. Using the game board that the majority of the class will be using, select six numbers and write them on the board.

2. Pick one of the numbers and secretly write it down on a piece of paper.

3. Ask the children to 'think, pair, share' some 'yes/no' questions that they could ask you to help them work out which of the numbers you have selected.

4. Let the children ask you the questions until they have established your chosen number. (You could discuss the effectiveness of each question and how they could be improved.)

5. Ensure children are confident with the place value names that they will need to use in the activity.

6. Share the poster prompt. Read through the rules together and ask any questions.

7. Give children time to play the game in similar ability pairs.

8. Once most children have finished a game, regroup the class. Discuss the questions they have been asking and how they could be refined. Now ask them to focus on strategies to 'win'. What numbers should they select as their number? What questions should they ask to eliminate numbers? Try to encourage children not to ask repeated place value related questions, but to explore other questions to eliminate numbers.

9. Finally, bring the children back together and discuss their 'winning strategies'.

Developing reasoning

➤ **What do you notice** about the value of the (2) in this number compared to this number?
➤ **What's the same? What's different** between (pick two or more numbers from the board)?
➤ Give me a **hard** number for your partner to guess. Give me an **easy** number for your partner to guess.
➤ Give me a number that has a (2 in its ones column/is higher than 4000). **Another, another, another.**

Providing differentiation

Support
Board 4 allows those children who still need to develop their place value up to HTU to take part in this activity. Children will also benefit from access to some of the practical resources mentioned in the 'background knowledge' section.

Extension
Board 3 is designed as an extension which introduces the children to decimal place value.

 Key strategies

2 Another, another, another
4 Hard and easy
7 Odd one out
10 What do you notice?
12 What's the same? What's different?

 Problem-solving approaches

Paired discussion is an effective approach for this problem.

Taking it further

The editable versions of the place value guess who grids, which you can find on the CD, can be used to create your own versions of the game, either with other numbers, or other mathematical terms, e.g. measures guess who, geometry guess who etc.

The place value guess who boards can also be used as a 'zooming in' board (see Key strategy 13, Zooming in) and could also be used as the basis for an ordering activity.

4 How much time?

Learning objective
- To solve problems involving converting between units of time.

Reasoning skills
- Working systematically
- Solving problems
- Conjecturing and convincing

Curriculum link
- Time: convert between units of time

The problem

> Problem 4
>
> ## How much time?
>
> There are often news articles about the amount of time children spend in front of 'screens', doing things like playing games, using computers and watching TV.
>
> How much time did you spend in front of a 'screen' yesterday?
>
> How much time will you spend in front of a screen over the next year? Would it be large enough for you to put into weeks? Or even months?
>
> If you put all the times together, how much time is your class likely to spend all together over the next year? Would this be large enough for you to put into years?
>
> **Your challenge**
>
> **Calculate how much screen time you will spend over the next week, next month and next year.**
>
> **Can you express this time in the largest time unit possible (days, hours, minutes, ...)?**
>
> **What do you find if you put all of the class's screen time together?**
>
> **Things to think about:**
> - How can you convert between different minutes of time? For example, how many minutes are there in an hour? In a day? In a month?
> - How are you going to predict your screen time over the next week? Month? Year?
> - How is it best to collect all of our screen time together?
>
>
>
> RISING STARS
> Maths
>
> Year 4 | Problem Solving and Reasoning

Background knowledge

- This investigation asks the children to predict how much 'screen time' they will have over the next week, month and year.
- They are then asked to work out the class's collective 'screen time' and to present it in the largest time unit possible.
- This will involve the children converting between units of time. They will need to be secure in the knowledge that:
  - there are 60 minutes in an hour
  - there are 24 hours in a day
  - there are 7 days in a week
  - there are 52 weeks in a year.
- The children should also be able to use these units to convert between other units of time,

e.g. work out that there are 168 hours in a week.
- The calculations involved in converting between units of time should largely be within the ability of a Year 4 child. However, a calculator could also be used to support calculation skills to maintain the focus on converting between units of time and statistics.
- If possible, begin by putting the investigation in context. There are invariably news stories and research published around 'screen time' or what children do in their spare time that could provide a good 'real-life' stimulus. Then show the children the prompt question.

Launching the activity

1. Show the prompt poster and estimate how much screen time they think they will have over the next year. *How much time as a class do you think we would spend in front of a screen over the next year?* Ask them to note their estimation so that they can compare it with the results of their investigation later. Note their estimation so it can be compared with the results later

2. Ask children to 'think, pair, share' with a partner what they need to know to solve the problem.

3. Ask them to discuss with a partner:
   a. how many minutes there are in an hour
   b. how many hours there are in a day
   c. how many days there are in a week
   d. how many weeks there are in a year.

4. Discuss and then pose the follow-up question: *If we know that there are 7 days in a week and 24 hours in a day, what else do we know?*

5. Ask the children how many weeks 42 days is. Discuss, and model if needed, how they have converted between units of time.

6. Give children time to work on the problem, discussing their working and thinking with a partner. Support children as needed.

7. Then ask them to estimate and share with a partner how much screen time, in minutes, they think they had last night.

8. Ask the children to calculate their individual screen time, then reconvene the class to discuss their findings and methods. How do they compare to their estimations?

9. Collate screen times to create a collective class figure. Ask children to discuss how to work out the second part of the challenge 'How much screen time we will have all together?' referring to the collective class figure.

10. In pairs, allow children to work out how much screen time the class will have over the next week, month and year.

11. Finally, ask children to compare the answers for the whole class problem together. How does it compare to their initial estimation?

Developing reasoning

➤ *What do you notice* about the numbers which you can make by multiplying two faces of a 1–6 dice together?
➤ *Convince me* that you will have spent xx time over the next week/four weeks/year.
➤ *Convince me* that there are 168 hours In a week.
➤ *Give me a silly answer* to this challenge. Why is it a silly answer?

Providing differentiation

Support
Let children use calculators during the investigative work. Also, they could just focus on the screen time over a week, then move on to four weeks

Extension
The children could be challenged to express the screen time in seconds, minutes, hours and, if appropriate, days, weeks and years.

 Key strategies

2 Another, another, another.
3 Convince me
10 What do you notice?

 Problem-solving approaches

Paired work

Taking it further

Screen time data could be analysed further with children investigating, e.g. whether boys or girls have more screen time, whether there is a difference in screen time based on children's bedtimes, whether other year groups have more or less screen time than children in Year 4, and so on.

5 Moving and shaping

Learning objective
- To solve problems involving perimeter.

Reasoning skills
- Working systematically
- Solving problems
- Conjecturing and convincinG

Curriculum link
📊 Measurement: calculate perimeter

The problem

Moving and shaping

Your teacher will give you a set of different shapes.

You must arrange the shapes so that they fit together to make one large shape.

Which way of arranging the shapes together would give you the smallest perimeter?

Which way would give you the largest?

You can arrange the shapes in any way you like, but the full sides of the shapes must be touching. For example,

you can have: :

Things to think about:
- What rules are you going to set yourself? For example, does the full length of the side of each shape have to touch the side of another shape?
- What type of shapes have the largest perimeter?
- How can you be sure you have found the largest and the smallest possible perimeter?
- If you had another of each shape, how would this effect the largest and smallest perimeters you could make?

Your challenge

Investigate the smallest and largest perimeter which it is possible to make by combining the shapes together.

Year 4 | Problem Solving and Reasoning

Background knowledge

- The children are asked to work out how to arrange a set of shapes to give the largest and smallest perimeter.
- Perimeter is the measure of the distance around a shape or area.
- Resource sheet 5.1, Shapes is provided for this activity. However, commercially-produced 2-D shapes or 'pattern blocks', could be used, providing the side lengths of these shapes are either full or half units and that they can be placed together.
- The children must ensure that sides of the shapes touch fully. Examples of what is and isn't 'allowed' are provided on the poster.
- The largest perimeter will be formed by arranging the shapes so that there is a large 'gap' in the middle of the shape.

- The smallest perimeter will be formed by arranging the shapes so that there is no gap in the middle of the shapes.
- The children can either measure the perimeter of the shapes, or place the shapes on cm² paper to help them calculate the perimeter.
- The children are also challenged to consider the impact of adding one more of each shape to the largest and smallest possible perimeters.
- The children could record their findings by taking photographs of each design or tracing around the edges of their designs. Tablet devices could also be used to photograph and annotate designs.

Launching the activity

1. Show the word 'perimeter' on the board and ask the children to think, pair, share its definition.

2. Discuss this together, creating a common definition.

3. Provide the children with one of the shapes from the activity. Ask them to calculate its perimeter. Discuss children's answers together.

4. Share the prompt question with the children.

5. Ask them to discuss the problem with their partner, and to come up with an initial response.

6. Discuss the children's initial thoughts together, recording any conjectures on the board or working wall.

7. Give children time to work through the activity, ideally working in mixed ability groups of three.

8. Then, ask each group to send an envoy to another group where they should share their findings and convince the other group that their arrangement of shapes generates the largest/ smallest perimeter.

9. Then ask, *If I had one more of each shape, would I be able to make a perimeter that is half as big again?* Provide time for them to discuss this in their groups, before discussing together.

Developing reasoning

➤ *What do you notice* about the perimeters which give you the larger/smaller perimeters?
➤ *Convince me* that you have found the largest and smallest perimeter.
➤ *What's the same? What's different* between your arrangement for the largest and smallest perimeter?

➤ *Give me an arrangement of these shapes that has a larger/smaller perimeter than the shape you have just created. Another, another, another.*
➤ *Give me a **peculiar and obvious** arrangement of these shapes that has a perimeter that is greater than/less than x cm.*
➤ *Give me a **silly answer** to this challenge. Why is it a silly answer?*

Providing differentiation

Support
The children should be encouraged to arrange their shapes on cm^2 paper to support them in calculating the perimeter.

The number of shapes could also be reduced, providing two of two different shapes.

Extension
The children could be challenged to calculate the area of the shapes they have made.

This could be further challenged by specifying that each arrangement of shapes they make must have a value for the perimeter that is greater than the area value.

Key strategies

3 Convince me
2 Another, another, another
8 Peculiar, obvious, general
9 Silly answers
10 What do you notice?

Problem-solving approaches

Group work; Think, pair, share

Taking it further

This activity could lead into further work on area (calculated by counting squares in Y4) and perimeter. For example, children could investigate different shapes which have numerically equal values for area and perimeter.

6 Would you rather?

Learning objective
- To solve problems involving fractions of number.

Reasoning skills
- Making comparisons
- Making connections

Curriculum link
½ Fractions: solve fraction problems

The problem

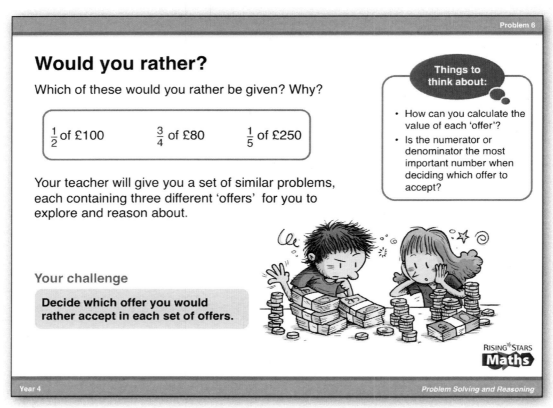

Would you rather?

Which of these would you rather be given? Why?

$\frac{1}{2}$ of £100 $\frac{3}{4}$ of £80 $\frac{1}{5}$ of £250

Your teacher will give you a set of similar problems, each containing three different 'offers' for you to explore and reason about.

Your challenge

Decide which offer you would rather accept in each set of offers.

Things to think about:
- How can you calculate the value of each 'offer'?
- Is the numerator or denominator the most important number when deciding which offer to accept?

Problem 6

Year 4   Problem Solving and Reasoning

RISING STARS Maths

Background knowledge

- The children are asked to compare different statements involving fractions of amounts to work out which they would rather 'receive'.
- To work out the fractions of these amounts, children will require previous experience of calculating fractions of number.
- Set 1 of the cards involves unit fractions only, whereas set 2 involves non-unit fractions. The last cards on both sets of fractions have statements which have the same value.
- It is important that children understand that a fraction represents the proportion of a number, so they develop a conceptual understanding of fractions and how to find fractions of number, rather than just following a set of 'rules'.
- They need to understand that the denominator (bottom number of a fraction) indicates how many equal groups their 'whole' is split into, and

that the numerator (top number of the fraction) indicates how many of these equal groups are needed. So ¾ means splitting the whole into 4 equal groups, of which 3 are needed.
- To find fractions of numbers, children first need to work out the size of their equal groups, which they can achieve by dividing their total by the denominator. Some children will benefit from having counters or cubes for this. They must look at the numerator to work out how many of these equal groups they need. Then, they find the amount the fraction represents by multiplying the value of the equal groups by the numerator.
- Practical resources such as counters, bead strings or other objects can really help to secure conceptual understanding by representing the problems visually. Fraction bars or strips (see Investigation 17, Fraction strips) can also be used, with the whole strip being given the value of which children are finding the proportion.

Launching the activity

1. Show 'fraction' on the board. Ask the children think, pair, share to create a definition of a fraction and share this with the class. Ensure the class identify that a fraction is a way of showing a proportion of an object, quantity or amount.

2. Display a fraction on the board. Ask the children to identify the names for the different elements of the fraction (numerator, denominator) and to define what they mean.

3. Introduce the problem. *Would you rather?* by John Burningham would provide a good introduction. If this is not available, display and discuss the prompt poster.

4. Ask the children for their initial response to the question on the prompt poster. Ask them to discuss their response with a partner, convincing them of their reasoning and thinking.

5. As a class, discuss some of their initial responses and their reasonings, noting any conjectures made.

6. If needed, recap how to find a fraction of a quantity.

7. Give the children time to work through the appropriate sets of cards, working with a partner to encourage mathematical talk. Draw their attention to the 'things to think about' questions on the prompt poster.

8. Finally, bring the children back together and discuss the 'things to think about' questions. Children could then be encouraged to set their own 'would you rather?' statements for a partner to solve.

Developing reasoning

➤ *What's the same? What's different* between *these statements?*
➤ *Which of these fractions of amounts is an* **odd one one out**? *Why?*
➤ *Is it* **always, sometimes or never** *true that the denominator is the most significant part to consider when answering these types of questions?*
➤ *Convince me* *that you would rather have* (pick a statement the children have said they would rather have).

Providing differentiation

Support
Children will benefit from using practical representations to explore and calculate the fractions of amounts, and may wish to focus on the first four cards in set 1, which provide slightly less challenge.

Extension
Challenge children to create their own 'would you rather?' statements for a partner to solve, focusing on ones that would be hard and easy to solve.

 Key strategies

2 Another, another, another
3 Convince me
9 Silly answers
10 What do you notice?
12 What's the same? What's different?

 Problem-solving approaches

Paired and group discussion.

Taking it further

This investigation could be used as a springboard to exploring real-life 'would you rather?' situations, e.g. of amounts of ingredients, food etc. Further work on fractions, focusing on equivalent fractions, could also follow and the fraction strips investigation would also work well before or after this investigation.

7 Tricky tangrams

Learning objective
- To solve problems by reasoning about shape.

Reasoning skills
- Working systematically
- Solving problems
- Conjecturing and convincing

Curriculum link
Properties of shapes: investigate shapes

The problem

Problem 7

Tricky tangrams

A tangram is a traditional Chinese puzzle, made up of seven different pieces.

'Tangram' means 'seven boards of skill'.

Your teacher will give you a sheet with these pieces on to make your own tangram set.

How many different polygons you can make using all seven pieces?

There are lots of different tangram challenges for you to explore!

You could start with the suggestions in the box.

Things to think about:
- Which pieces fit together well?
- Are there any polygons that you cannot make?
- What are the properties of the different shapes you have made?

Ideas to get you started
- One square
- A right-angle triangle
- Two squares that are equal in size

Your challenge

> Investigate which different polygons you can make using all seven tangram pieces.

RISING STARS
Maths

Year 4   Problem Solving and Reasoning

Background knowledge

- This problem revolves around the traditional Chinese 'tangram' puzzle.
- 'Tangram' can be literally translated to mean 'seven boards of skill'.
- A tangram set is provided on the CD-ROM on Resource sheet 7.1, Tangram, for you to photocopy for each child. Each tangram set is made up of 7 shapes.
- The tangram pieces can be assembled to create different shapes.
- This puzzle challenges children to create as many different polygons as they can using the tangram pieces.

- There are numerous possible solutions. the children should be encouraged to name each polygon they have created and identify some of its properties.
- The children should ideally be able to photograph each of their solutions. They could then use a range of different ICT applications to create a poster or slideshow of their solutions.
- The challenge poster provides three specific challenges to get children started using their tangram pieces. Some possible solutions to each challenge are shown on Resource sheet 7.2, Tangram solutions.

Launching the activity

1. Provide each pair with a tangram set, ideally already cut up.

2. Ask each pair to identify the different shapes that make up the tangram set, then discuss these together, ensuring children are able to name each shape that makes up the tangram set.

3. Explain the origins of the tangram puzzle. Ask the children if they can arrange the tangrams into one square.

4. Share each pair's solution to this first challenge.

5. Share the poster prompt with the children.

6. Ask them to discuss the problem with their partner, and to come up with an initial strategy for the problem.

7. Give children time to work through the activity, working in pairs, encouraging them to name the shape properties of any shapes they create.

8. After the children have had time to work on the activity, discuss the solutions to the specific challenges from the prompt together.

9. After further working time, ask the children to switch partners. Ask them to set their new partner a Tangram challenge based on their findings from the main investigation, (e.g. *Can you create an irregular hexagon?*)

10. Finally, discuss the children's solutions together, perhaps asking them to set further questions which they could investigate in subsequent sessions, (e.g. *I wonder how many sides it is possible to make a polygon with out of a tangram set?*)

Developing reasoning

> ➤ *What do you notice* about way the shapes arrange together?
> ➤ *What's the same? What's different* between (pick two polygons created)?
> ➤ *Give me another way to make* (pick a polygon that the children have created). *Another, another, another.*
> ➤ *Give me a peculiar and obvious* arrangement of these pieces.

Providing differentiation

Support
The children may find that the three problems provided on the prompt poster will provide enough material for them to work on during the whole lesson.

Extension
The children could be asked to investigate the different polygons possible to make if you didn't have to use all 7 pieces.

 ## Key strategies

2   Another, another, another
8   Peculiar, obvious, general
10 What do you notice?
12 What's the same? What's different?

 ## Problem-solving approaches

Group work; Think, pair, share

Taking it further

There is plenty of scope for further sessions exploring tangrams. Children's questions created during the last stage of the activity could be investigated in subsequent sessions. Further tangram challenges can also be found at http://www.funorama.com/tangram-challenges-1.html and http://www.tangram-channel.com/

8 | A dicey game

Learning objective	Reasoning skills	Curriculum link
• To solve problems involving multiplication by making generalisations.	• Working systematically • Solving problems • Conjecturing and convincing	**1.3** Multiplication and division: generalise about products

The problem

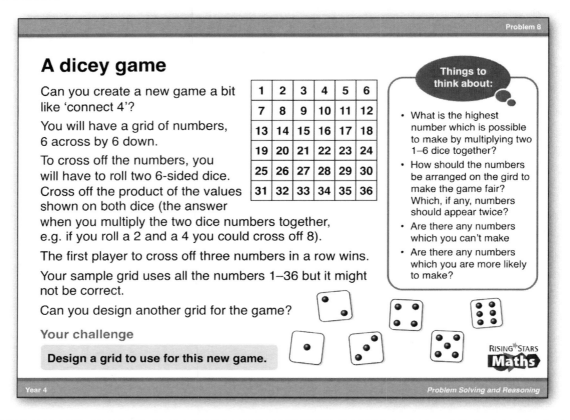

A dicey game

Can you create a new game a bit like 'connect 4'?

You will have a grid of numbers, 6 across by 6 down.

To cross off the numbers, you will have to roll two 6-sided dice. Cross off the product of the values shown on both dice (the answer when you multiply the two dice numbers together, e.g. if you roll a 2 and a 4 you could cross off 8).

The first player to cross off three numbers in a row wins.

Your sample grid uses all the numbers 1–36 but it might not be correct.

Can you design another grid for the game?

1	2	3	4	5	6
7	8	9	10	11	12
13	14	15	16	17	18
19	20	21	22	23	24
25	26	27	28	29	30
31	32	33	34	35	36

Things to think about:

• What is the highest number which is possible to make by multiplying two 1–6 dice together?
• How should the numbers be arranged on the gird to make the game fair? Which, if any, numbers should appear twice?
• Are there any numbers which you can't make
• Are there any numbers which you are more likely to make?

Your challenge

Design a grid to use for this new game.

RISING STARS
Maths

Year 4 | Problem Solving and Reasoning

Background knowledge

• This investigation asks the children to help design a new game, based on the product of two 1–6 dice faces.

• Not all numbers between 1 and 36 are possible to make from the product of two numbers between 1 and 6. Some numbers which are impossible to make are: 11, 13, 14, 17, 19, 22, 23, 26, 27, 28, 29, 31, 32, 33, 34, 35.

Launching the activity

1. Introduce the problem using the prompt poster, asking for help in designing a new game.

2. Ask the children what 'product' means. Establish that this is the result of multiplying two (or more) numbers together.

3. Show children the grid design (1–36) on Resource sheet 8.1, The original grid. Ask why it stops at 36 (the maximum product is 36 (6 × 6). Ask them to discuss this with a partner. *Is this a sensible design for the game grid?*

4. Discuss this together. Establish that some numbers are impossible to roll and therefore do not need to be on the grid.

5. Ask the children what the first number that you cannot possibly make is. Establish that it is 11.

6. Set the children off on the main task, working in mixed ability groups, ideally using 'graffiti maths'.

7. Partway through the session, bring the class back together. Discuss the different strategies used so far. *What has been effective?* Discuss the numbers that are impossible to make.

8. Discuss the second part of the problem: which numbers should be on the grid more than once? Discuss that some numbers are more likely to be made than others, e.g. 12 can be made in four ways (2 and 6, 3 and 4, 6 and 2, 4 and 3).

9. Allow the children time to work together on the problem using Resource sheet 8.2, Blank grid.

10. At the end of the session share each group's final grid. Use the 'envoy' approach to allow children to share with another group the reasons behind the design of their grids.

Developing reasoning

➤ *How are you going to record your answers?*
➤ *How are you going to organise your group so that it works most effectively?*
➤ **What do you notice** *about the numbers which you can make by multiplying two faces of a 1–6 dice together?*
➤ **Convince me** *that 13 shouldn't be on the grid.*
➤ **Convince me** *that 12 should be on the grid more than 36.*
➤ *Give me a way you could make 6.* **Another, another and another.**

Providing differentiation

Support
The children could use a multiplication square to help them explore this problem, focusing on the 1–6 section.

Extension
More able children should begin to discuss the second part of the problem much sooner than most children.

They could also extend the activity by using a 1–10 dice together with a 1–6 dice, which gives many more possible products and distributions. Two 1–10 dice can then be used to extend the problem further.

 Key strategies

2 Another, another, another.
3 Convince me
10 What do you notice?

 Problem-solving approaches

Graffiti maths and the envoy approach work particularly well for this problem.

Taking it further

This activity could be extended to other game creation scenarios.

Learning objective
- To investigate patterns in numbers and calculations.

Reasoning skills
- Conjecturing and convincing
- Making generalisations

Curriculum link
1.3 Addition and subtraction: investigate patterns

The problem

Problem 9

Finding the difference

From a set of digit cards containing the digits 1–9, take three cards and arrange them into the biggest number possible, e.g. with 4, 5 and 7 you would make 754.

Then using the same three cards, make the smallest number possible, e.g. 457.

Then find the difference between these two numbers, e.g. 754 – 457.

What do you notice about your answer?

Things to think about:

- What do you notice about the difference if you use consecutive numbers? (numbers that follow each other, e.g. 3, 4, 5)
- Is there anything that links the differences between your sets of numbers?
- Is there is a link? Can you begin to reason why this link may exist?

Your challenge

Explore what happens when you take the biggest number that is it possible to make out of three digits, from the smallest number.
Are there any rules, patterns or generalisations?

Hint: First, explore the difference between 2-digit numbers and see if anything you notice is the same for 3-digit numbers.

RISING STARS
Maths

Year 4

Problem Solving and Reasoning

Background knowledge

- The children are asked to investigate what happens when you subtract a 3-digit number from its reverse, e.g. subtracting 678 from 876 (876 – 678 = 198).
- When subtracting a 3-digit number from its reverse, the answer is always a multiple of 9.
- The explanation is probably beyond Year 4, but for your information:
  - Any 3-digit number can be represented as: $100A + 10B + C$
  - The number reversed is: $100C + 10B + A$
  - The difference: $(100A + 10B + C) - (100C + 10B + A) = 99A - 99C = 99(A-C)$
  - As the answer is always 99 multiplied by (A–C) and 99 itself is a multiple of 9, then the answer will always be a multiple of 9.

- Children should first investigate the difference between a 2-digit number and its reverse. This is also always a multiple of 9.
- As the result of subtracting the 3-digit number and its reverse is always a multiple of 9, the digit root (keep adding the digits in the number together until you end with a single-digit number) will also always be 9.
- As an extra bit of 'maths trivia', if you add the resulting 3-digit number to its reverse, e.g. 198 + 981 in our example above, the answer will always be 1089, unless the starting number has the same first and third digit.

Launching the activity

1. Ask the children to write down any 3-digit number. Ask them then to write down its reverse and subtract it from their initial number. Then ask children to compare their results with a partner. Ask, *What's the same? What's different?*

2. Discuss the findings from this initial activity as a class.

3. Then introduce the problem by sharing the prompt poster.

4. Ask the children to discuss with a partner a possible approach for tackling the problem and discuss these as a class, ensuring that the suggestion (as provided on the poster) of starting with 2-digit numbers and looking at any generalisations is mentioned.

5. Give the children the majority of the lesson to work on the activity, preferably in groups of three, stressing the key question, *What do you notice?* Support individual groups as needed.

6. Midway through the session reconvene the class and discuss any conjectures that they have made so far.

7. At the end of the session bring the children back together to share what they have noticed and any generalisations they have made.

Developing reasoning

➤ ***What do you notice*** about the results of subtracting these two numbers from each other?
➤ ***Convince me*** that your conjecture/generalisation is true.
➤ ***What's the same? What's different*** between these two numbers?

Providing differentiation

Support
The children may wish to focus solely on investigating what happens when you subtract a 2-digit number from its reverse.

Extension
The children can test their generalisations further to see if this extends to 4- or 5-digit numbers. They could also investigate what happens if they subtract a U.tu number from its reverse.

 Key strategies

  3 Convince me
10 What do you notice?
12 What's the same? What's different?

 Problem-solving approaches

Paired work; Graffiti maths

Taking it further

This activity could lead into further investigations into properties of number. Investigation 2, A bit of magic and Investigation 15, Terrific thirty-six would link well with this activity.

10 Highest and lowest

<table>
<tr>
<td>

Learning objective
• To work together to solve a problem.

</td>
<td>

Reasoning skills
• Spotting patterns
• Working systematically
• Solving problems

</td>
<td>

Curriculum link
1,2,3 Number and place value: place value in 4-digit numbers

</td>
</tr>
</table>

The problem

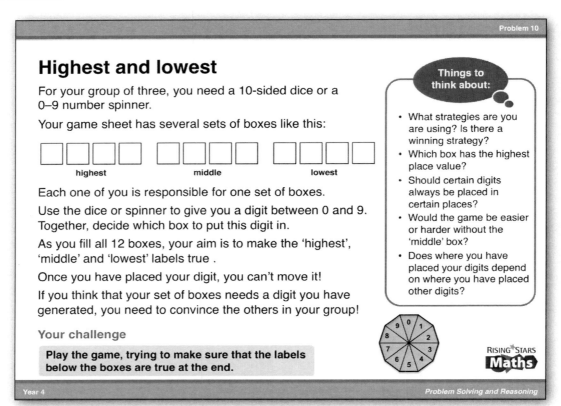

Highest and lowest

For your group of three, you need a 10-sided dice or a 0–9 number spinner.

Your game sheet has several sets of boxes like this:

□□□□   □□□□   □□□□
highest   middle   lowest

Each one of you is responsible for one set of boxes.

Use the dice or spinner to give you a digit between 0 and 9. Together, decide which box to put this digit in.

As you fill all 12 boxes, your aim is to make the 'highest', 'middle' and 'lowest' labels true .

Once you have placed your digit, you can't move it!

If you think that your set of boxes needs a digit you have generated, you need to convince the others in your group!

Your challenge

Play the game, trying to make sure that the labels below the boxes are true at the end.

Things to think about:

• What strategies are you are using? Is there a winning strategy?
• Which box has the highest place value?
• Should certain digits always be placed in certain places?
• Would the game be easier or harder without the 'middle' box?
• Does where you have placed your digits depend on where you have placed other digits?

RISING STARS
Maths

Year 4   Problem Solving and Reasoning

Background knowledge

• This investigation takes the form of a co-operative game which challenges children to generate digits and put them into placeholders to create three 4-digit numbers.
• Their aim is to make sure that all three numbers conform to the 'highest', 'middle', 'lowest' labels given to them.
• Once the children have placed the digit that they have generated, they cannot move it.
• The children will need to reason about the best place for them to place each digit they have generated to have the greatest chance of their final set of numbers conforming to the labels given.

• The children need to discuss each digit placement together, convincing each other of the best place for each digit.
• Through discussion, the children should be encouraged to consider the best 'rules' to give the best chance of creating three numbers which conform to the labels. For example, they may decide that they should always place the digit 9 in the highest value place that is available in the 'highest' number, and the digit 0 in the highest possible place in the 'lowest' number.
• Children will, of course, have to consider the place value that each digit 'attracts' when they are placed in different places in the number.

Launching the activity

1. Model a competitive version of the game with the class (you could play against the class or split the class in half). Write up four placeholders for each 'team' on the board.

   ___ ___ ___ ___

2. Explain that the aim of the game is to create the biggest number possible. Each team will take turns to roll a dice/spin a spinner (see Resource sheet 10.1, Number spinner 0–9) to generate a digit. They then place the digit in one of their placeholders.

3. Play this version of the game together, repeating as necessary.

4. Ask the children to think, pair, share with a partner what strategies they could use for this game. Discuss these as a class, ensuring that place value is discussed.

5. Explain that they are going to play a different version of this game. Introduce the game using the prompt poster.

6. In groups of three, give the children time to discuss their approaches to the problem.

7. Using Resource sheet 10.2, Highest, middle, lowest, allow plenty of time for children to explore the problem and play the game several times. Stress that they should think about 'rules' to give themselves the best chance of winning.

8. At the end of the session, bring the children back together. Ask each group to share one of the rules they have been using to stand the greatest chance of completing the challenge.

Developing reasoning

➤ **What do you notice** about the value of the (3) when placed here or here?

➤ **What's the same? What's different** between placing (3) in this number?

➤ Give me a **hard** digit to place. Give me an **easy** digit to place. Why is this **hard** or **easy**?

➤ Is it **always, sometimes or never** true that you should always place the digit 8 or 9 in the 'highest' number place holders?

Providing differentiation

Support
The children will benefit from using place value (Gattengo) charts to support them with the place value element of this activity.

Children could also use the adapted game board which uses just HTU numbers.

Extension
The children could use the amended game board on Resource sheet 10.2, Highest, middle, lowest (with decimals) which uses TU.tu numbers. Children should be encouraged to make higher level generalisations, and could be challenge to write an 'algorithm' to solve the puzzle, e.g. If you generate a 2, try and place it in the lowest number; if you cannot do this, place it in the lowest value place in the middle number. If you draw a 3 … .

Key strategies

2 Another, another, another
4 Hard and easy
10 What do you notice?
12 What's the same? What's different?

Problem-solving approaches

Paired and group discussion.

Taking it further

Further work on place value could be carried out using Investigation 3, Place value guess who.

This game can also be adapted in many other ways, e.g. you can play the version of the game from the shared learning, but allow each player to place the digit they generate in either their own or their partner's placeholders.

11 Disco drinks

Learning objective
- To work systematically to find all possibilities involving addition and subtraction.

Reasoning skills
- Working systematically
- Solving problems
- Conjecturing and convincing

Curriculum link
1,3 Addition and subtraction: calculate with money

The problem

> **Problem 11**
>
> ## Disco drinks
>
> Dancing is thirsty work so your next school disco will need a drinks stall.
>
> Imagine that the stall will sell the drinks listed.
>
> Kirsty and her four friends each have £1.50 each to spend.
>
> **Drinks menu**
> - 150 ml cartons of bubble gum favoured drink (14p each)
> - 200 ml bottles of cherry aid (16p each)
> - 330 ml cans of lemonade (53p each)
> - 500 ml bottles of cola (57p each)
> - 200 ml bottles of limeade (23p each)
> - 200 ml cartons of orange juice (27p each)
> - 200 ml cans of rainbow disco drink (43p each)
>
> **Things to think about:**
> - Is there more than one possible solution for each challenge?
> - Does it matter if the cost of the drinks is odd or even?
>
> **Your challenge**
>
> **Work out all the possibilities for:**
> - what Kirsty could buy if she spends all of her money on 4 drinks.
> - what combinations Riley could buy if he buys over 6 drinks, but spends all of his money.
> - what different combinations Harry could buy if he spends 10p on sweets and the rest on drinks. He doesn't like cola.
> - what Max could buy if he saved 30p to spend on sweets and buys only two different types of drink.
> - what combinations Shayla could buy if she ends the night with 7p left.
>
> **Extra challenge**
> Can you create your own similar problems for a friend to solve?
>
>
>
> Year 4   *Problem Solving and Reasoning*

Background knowledge

- This problem asks children to work systematically to investigate possible combinations that meet a set of criteria.
- The problem also involves children calculating with money, including crossing the £1 boundary, a skill with which they should already be secure in Year 4.

- For each challenge on the poster there is more than one possible solution.
- The prices of the drinks have been set so that they can combine to make multiples of 10p. This is a key element which, once realised, will help in solving the challenge, e.g. lemonade (53p) and orange juice (27p) can be combined to make a total spend of 80p.

Launching the activity

1. Introduce the problem by sharing the problem poster, setting it in a recent context if possible.

2. Ask the children to think, pair, share. *If you spent 80p at the drink stall, what possible combinations of drinks could you have bought?*

3. Discuss possible combinations together, ensuring that children realise there two possible combinations (cola + limeade, lemonade + orange juice).

4. Allow time for children to work in pairs on the main challenge questions from the prompt poster.

5. After a short while, bring children back together for a mini-plenary and share possible solutions for the first challenge. You may also want to highlight and model any effective ways of recording developed by the children.

6. Once children have solved the problems on the poster, they should then focus on creating their own problems based on the drinks stall for others to solve.

7. At the end of the session, bring children back together and discuss their solutions for the different challenges and effective ways of working. If time allows, as a class, attempt some of the challenges created by the children.

Developing reasoning

➤ ***What do you notice*** about the price of the different drinks? Are there any 'good' combinations to use?
➤ ***Convince me*** that you have found all the possible solutions.
➤ Give me a way you could spend (XXp). ***Another, another, another.***
➤ Give me a ***hard and easy*** question based on the drinks stall. Why is it hard/easy?
➤ Give me a ***silly answer*** to this the problem posed on the poster. Why is it a silly answer?

Providing differentiation

Support
Children would benefit from using coins to help them represent the values and combinations in this problem.

Extension
Children could be encouraged to create their own problems, which combine both the price and capacity information provided on the poster.

Key strategies

2 Another, another, another
3 Convince me
4 Hard and easy
9 Silly answers
10 What do you notice?

Problem-solving approaches

Paired work

Taking it further

This activity could lead into further investigations which involve systematic working, particularly Investigation 12, Mystery numbers.

Mystery numbers

Learning objective
• To investigate relationships between numbers.

Reasoning skills
• Solving problems
• Working systematically
• Finding all possibilities

Curriculum link
1 2 Addition and subtraction: properties of number

The problem

Problem 12

Mystery numbers

Jacob has a set of ten cards with these numbers on:

| 10 | 11 | 12 | 13 | 14 | 15 | 16 | 17 | 18 | 19 |

He shuffled the cards and gave two to each of his friends.

His friends told him the sum (total) of the two numbers they were given.

Adam said his cards total **28.**

Josh said his cards total **24.**

Ellie said her cards total **33.**

Emily said her cards total **34.**

Olivia said her cards total **26.**

Things to think about:
• Is there more than one possible solution?
• Is there more than one way to make each total?
• Do all numbers have the same number of possible ways to make them?
• Would it be easier or harder to solve if I had nine cards and three friends each with three cards? Why?

Your challenge

Work out which cards each of Jacob's friends are holding.

RISING STARS
Maths

Year 4 — Problem Solving and Reasoning

Background knowledge

• This challenge asks children to identify which possible pairs of numbers (from 10–19) could combine to make certain totals.
• The children need to work systematically in order to solve this problem.
• The problem can be solved in many different ways. Children may, however, find it easiest to list all the possible combinations for each number, working systemically by increasing one number whilst reducing the other, e.g.

28	24	33	34	26
10 + 18	10 + 14	19 + 14	19 + 15	10 + 16
11 + 17	11 + 13	18 + 15	18 + 16	11 + 15
12 + 16		17 + 16		12 + 14
13 + 15				

• The children can then use this information to find sets of cards which do not involve duplicated cards. This leads to there only being one solution.

28	10 + 18
24	11 + 13
33	17 + 16
34	19 + 15
26	12 + 14

Launching the activity

1. Begin by showing the class cards displaying the numbers 10, 11, 12, 13, 14, 15. Ask for three volunteers.

2. Show the class that you are going to give one child cards 15 and 12. Give the cards to the child and ask the class for the total of the cards that this child is holding (27). Next give another child cards 14 and 11, without showing the class. Ask this second child to tell the class their total (25).

3. Ask the remainder of the children to think, pair and share. *What cards could the second child be holding?* Discuss this together. *Why couldn't it be 10 + 15 or 12 + 13?*

4. Ask what the total of the third volunteer's cards would be (13 + 11 = 24).

5. Share the prompt poster with the children. Give them some thinking time about how they could possibly attempt to solve the problem, before sharing their thoughts with a partner.

6. During the majority of the session, allow children to work on the problem in pairs, visiting each pair to develop their thinking.

7. At an appropriate point, ask the children to pause. Share some approaches and things that they have noticed so far.

8. At the end of the session, ask everyone to form new pairs and share their solution and ways of arriving at it with their new partner. What was the same? What was different about their approaches?

Developing reasoning

> *What do you notice* about the number of ways in which you can make each of the numbers?
> Give me *silly answer* for this problem.
> *Convince me* that (Mo) has to have the xx card.
> Give me a way to make xx out of the cards. *Another, another, another.*
> If we say that (Carrie) *has the xx and* yy *cards what else do we know?*

Providing differentiation

Support
Use the number cards provided on Resource sheet 12.1 Number cards, which will provide a way for the children to try out different solutions easily and ensure that numbers are duplicated.

Extension
The children should progress to creating their own, similar, problems for a partner to solve. They could be challenged to create an 'easy' and 'hard' problem, or one which has more than one possible solution.

 Key strategies

3 Convince me
8 Peculiar, obvious, general
10 What do you notice?
11 What else do we know?
12 What's the same? What's different?

 Problem-solving approaches

Paired work; think, pair, share; envoys

Taking it further

The children could explore problems which involve them working systematically, e.g. Investigation 13, Crack the code.

13 Crack the code!

Learning objective
- To solve problems involving multiplication skills.

Reasoning skills
- Reasoning algebraically
- Solving problems
- Making connections

Curriculum link
13 Multiplication and division: properties of number

The problem

Crack the code

Your teacher will give you a set of sheets with different multiplication tables on them.

But the digits in the tables have been replaced by letters.

For example, A *could* stand for the digit 2, B *could* stand for the digit 4, etc.

Each times table sheet has its own code.

This means that the letter A does not necessarily have the same value on all the sheets.

Of course, the times tables are all jumbled up on each sheet – it's not just 1 × 2, 2 × 2, 3 × 2, etc.

That would be too easy!

Things to think about:

- Is there any multiplication statement that will help you work out the value of some of the letters straightaway?
- How many single- and double-digit answers are there?
- Once you have cracked what digits a few letters represent, does this help you work out what the rest represent?

Your challenge

Work out which times table is represented on each sheet and which digit each letter stands for.

Extra challenge

Can you create your own mystery times table for a partner to solve? How are you going to make sure it is solvable?

RISING STARS
Maths

Year 4   Problem Solving and Reasoning

Background knowledge

- This challenge provides the children with a set of times tables, where the digits have been substituted for letters.
- In each times table, each letter stands for a different digit. However, letters can stand for other digits in other times tables, e.g. the value of A is not the same in times tables 1 and 2. Note, the letter I is not used to avoid confusion with the number 1.
- In order to 'crack the code' children need to reason about properties of multiplication facts/tables.
- Once children have identified the value of one letter, they should substitute this wherever this letter appears. Once the children have identified one value, the rest of the code becomes significantly easier to crack.

- For example, in the B times table on Resource sheet 13.1, children can infer that B must be 5 or more. This is because there is only one times table fact that has a single-digit answer.
- The children should then notice that the last two digits are either B or K. They should make the connection to the 5 times table, whose last digits alternate between 5 and 10. This therefore means that the B times table is the 5 times table, that the letter B represents 5 and K represents 0.
- Answers to B, C and G times tables:
  13.1 B=5, A=3, C=9, D=8, E=7, F=4, G=2, H=6, J=1, K=0; **13.2** C=6, A=2, B=3, D=1, E=4, F=7, G=5, H=8, J=9, K=0; **13.3** G=8, A=2, B=3, C=6, D=1, E=5, F=7, H=0, J=4, K=9.

Launching the activity

1. Begin by showing the prompt poster and the B times table. Give children time to think, pair, share a possible approach to solving this problem.

2. Discuss their suggestions and their initial thoughts together, making a note on the board or working wall of any conjectures or statements made.

3. Allow the majority of the session for the children to work in pairs on the problem on Resource sheets 13.1, 13.2 and 13.3. Crack the code.

4. Whilst children are working, visit each pair and ask questions to develop their reasoning further.

5. At an appropriate point, bring the class briefly back together and discuss strategies which the children have been using so far.

6. Towards the end of the session, bring the children back together and share their answers to each times table, inviting pairs to answer the question, *How do you know?* to convince the whole class that their response is correct.

7. Children can then be challenged to create their own mystery times table for a partner to solve.

Developing reasoning

➤ **What do you notice** about the digits/letters in this times table? **What do you notice** about where the letter X appears?

➤ Give me a **silly answer** for what times table this is. Why is this silly?

➤ Is it **always, sometimes or never** true that in order to crack the code, the first letter you should crack is the one whose times table you are looking at?

➤ **Convince me** that this is the x times table/that this couldn't be the y times table.

➤ Set a **hard and easy** times table code for your partner to crack.

Providing differentiation

Support
The children may benefit from referring to a multiplication grid during this activity in order to compare patterns between the grid and the coded tables.

Extension
The children should progress onto creating their own code element of the activity fairly quickly. They should be encouraged to think and reason about what makes a times table easy and hard to crack and to convince each other of the hardest times table to crack.

 Key strategies

3 Convince me
4 Hard and easy
10 What do you notice?
11 What else do we know?
12 What's the same? What's different?

 Problem-solving approaches

Mixed ability group work; Graffiti maths

Taking it further

This activity could be used as the springboard into a series of sessions focusing on developing children's ability to reason algebraically.

14 Symmetry squared

The problem

Crack the code

Jodie has made a 4 × 4 grid on squared paper.

She started to think about how many different symmetrical patterns she could possibly make by shading in some squares on her grid.

For example, she could shade in 4 squares like this to make a symmetrical pattern.

Things to think about:

- How many lines of symmetry are there in the unshaded square? Can you use these to help you identify lines of symmetry when you have shaded different sections?
- How are you going to make sure you have found all possible solutions?
- Is it possible to make a symmetrical pattern by shading an odd number of squares?

Your challenge

Find as many different ways as you can of making patterns which have at least one line of reflective symmetry using a 4 × 4 grid.

RISING STARS
Maths

Year 4   Problem Solving and Reasoning

Background knowledge

- Children are asked to find all the possible ways to shade a 4 × 4 square so that the square has reflective symmetry.
- Reflective symmetry is a type of symmetry where one half of an object or pattern is the mirror image of the other half.
- Children will need to develop a systematic approach to find all possible designs. For example, they may wish to consider all designs possible when they shade just one square, then all designs possible when shading just two squares etc.
- Resource sheet 14.1, 4 × 4 grids is provided on the CD.

- Children will need to explore all four lines of reflective symmetry in the square.
- Children will need to consider how to best organise their group so that they can find

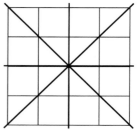

all possible designs. They may, for example, decide that each of them focuses on a different line of symmetry or on a different number of shaded blocks.

Launching the activity

1. Write 'reflective symmetry' on the board. Ask children to 'think, pair, share' to create its definition and share this with the class.

2. If needed, model different patterns and shapes which have reflective symmetry.

3. Give children Resource sheet 14.1, 4 × 4 grids. Ask each child to shade some squares on one of the grids so that their resulting pattern has a line of reflective symmetry.

4. Ask them to compare their shaded pattern with their partner, and discuss what's the same and what's different. Then ask each partner to share their two designs with another pair. Discuss how different children have created different patterns, but how they all have reflective symmetry.

5. Share the prompt poster with the children. Ask them to estimate an answer to the problem.

6. Give children time to discuss possible ways of working with their partner and share some of these approaches with the class.

7. Display Resource sheet 14.2, Large 4 × 4 grid. Ask, *How many lines of reflective symmetry does the blank grid have?* Establish that it has four lines of reflective symmetry and therefore children may want to investigate patterns which are based around each different line.

8. Give children time to work on the problem, ideally working in mixed ability groups. Encourage them to consider how they are organising their group and working together.

9. Finally, bring the children back together and discuss their approaches to the problem and the solutions they have found.

Developing reasoning

➤ ***What do you notice*** about the symmetry in this design?
➤ ***What's the same? What's different*** between these two solutions?
➤ Give me a **peculiar** and **obvious** design that has reflective symmetry.
➤ Give me a design that uses three shaded squares. **Another, another, another.**
➤ Which of your designs is the **odd one out?** Why?
➤ Give me a **silly answer** for a design that has a line of reflective symmetry.
➤ If we know that this design has reflective symmetry, **what else do we know?**

Providing differentiation

Support
Children will benefit from using mirrors in order to check their lines of reflective symmetry. Children may also benefit from being challenged just to find the number of possible designs formed by shading three (or another number) squares.

Extension
Children can be challenged to find all the possible designs that have two lines of symmetry.

 Key strategies

2   Another, another, another
7   Odd one out
8   Peculiar, obvious, general
10 What do you notice?
12 What's the same? What's different?

 Problem-solving approaches

Paired and group discussion

Taking it further

Further work on symmetry could follow this investigation. Children could, for example, investigate symmetry in real life, perhaps through a maths trial. Children could also be challenged to find the lines of reflective symmetry in each letter of the alphabet or in different countries' flags, etc.

15 Terrific thirty-six

Learning objective
- To solve investigate properties, patterns and relationships of numbers.

Reasoning skills
- Working systematically
- Solving problems

Curriculum link
L3 Number and place value: properties of numbers

The problem

Problem 15

Terrific thirty-six

Today, my favourite number is 36.

I wonder how many different statements and/or statements we could write that have the answer 36?

Your challenge

Create as many different statements and/or questions as you can which have the answer 36.

Extra challenges

- Write five questions that also involve the number 72.
- Write some questions in a context.
- Write some statements that involve two different operations.
- Write a question that involve the < or > sign.
- Write some statements that involve a fraction.
- Write some statements that involve a decimal.

Things to think about:

- Can you use any patterns to help you?
- Are there an infinite number of questions and statements which have the answer 36?
- How could you include a fraction or decimal in your questions/statements?

36 36 36 36

RISING STARS **Maths**

Year 4 · Problem Solving and Reasoning

Background knowledge

- This problem asks children to investigate the number 36, by generating as many different possible questions or statements to which the 'answer' is 36.
- This is a combination and extension of the 'If this is the answer, what's the question?' and 'maths stories' key strategies, so these sections should be read before leading this activity.
- Children should be encouraged to spot and continue patterns in order to create related questions/statements easily, e.g.
  - $2 \times 18 = 36$
  - $4 \times 9 = 36$
  - $8 \times 4.5 = 36$
  - $16 \times 2.25 = 36$
  - $1 \times 36 = 36$
  - $0.5 \times 36 = 36$
- On the poster some suggested challenge questions are provided; similar prompt questions can be created as needed. Children can also be encouraged to set each other challenges.
- Children should be encouraged to make a wide range of statements, which involve many areas of mathematics. Combined with focused questioning, this activity can therefore provide a very good opportunity for assessment of a wide range of different areas of mathematics.

Launching the activity

1. Begin by showing the number 36 on the board. Give children two minutes to write down as many different things that they know about 36 as they can (the story of 36).

2. Ask children to compare their 'stories' with a partner. Have they all written similar things?

3. Share some statements from the children's 'stories' as a class, recording them on the board and/or working wall.

4. Share the prompt poster with the children. Give children a short time to discuss the prompt poster together.

5. Give children most of the session to work in mixed ability groups (of three or four) on this challenge. Stress that all children in each group must understand a statement/question before it is written down. Graffiti maths provides a particular effective way of working for this investigation.

6. Whilst children are working, provide further prompts/challenge questions to further develop their thinking and reasoning.

7. Towards the end of the session bring the children back together. Ask each group to share a peculiar and obvious statement/question which they have written and explain why this is peculiar/obvious.

Developing reasoning

➤ **What do you notice** about the number 36? This calculation?
➤ Give me a **hard and easy** statement/question that has the answer 36.
➤ Give me a **peculiar** and **obvious** statement/question?

➤ Can you give a related statement/question to this one? **Another, another, another.** How are they related?
➤ **Convince me** that these numbers do/do not combine to make 100.
➤ If we know that (pick statement made by the children), **what else do we know?**

Providing differentiation

Support
Working in mixed ability groups, as suggested above, should provide peer support for children who are less confident. Children could also be encouraged to continue simple patterns, e.g. they could be provided with the statements 2 + 34 = 36, 3 + 33 = 36, 4 + 32 = 36 and be asked to continue them.

Extension
Children should be given increasingly more complex challenge questions, e.g. can you give me a statement which involves a number less than 0.1?, can you give me a question/statement which has two numbers but both of these numbers are the same (e.g. 6 × 6 = 36).

Key strategies

3 Convince me
4 Hard and easy
8 Peculiar, obvious, general
10 What do you notice?
11 What else do we know?

Problem-solving approaches

Mixed ability group work; graffiti maths

Taking it further

This activity can easily be extended to other numbers and mathematical concepts. See the Key strategy sections for more ideas.

16 Double double

Learning objective
- To investigate patterns in number sequences.

Reasoning skills
- Working systematically
- Solving problems
- Conjecturing and convincing

Curriculum link
1·3 Number and place value: sequences

The problem

Problem 16

Double double

If you started with the number 2 and kept doubling it, you would soon get to a number which is over 100:

$$2 \rightarrow 4 \rightarrow 8 \rightarrow 16 \rightarrow 32 \rightarrow 64 \rightarrow 128$$

You could continue this chain and you would soon be over 1000.

Look at the doubling chain. Can you spot any patterns?

Do the patterns exist when you start by doubling another number?

Things to think about:

- What do you notice about the digits in your double chains?
- Starting with the number 2, you get over 100 after 7 doubles. Is this the same for all single-digit numbers? Are there any patterns in how many doubles it takes to get over 100?
- Are all the doubles always even?

Your challenge

Investigate patterns formed by constantly doubling. First, you could investigate patterns that are formed when you start with a single-digit number.

RISING STARS
Maths

Year 4 · Problem Solving and Reasoning

Background knowledge

- This open-ended investigation essentially asks children, *What do you notice?* when constantly doubling numbers, starting at different starting points.
- It also provides a good opportunity for children to practise their doubling skills. Children should be encouraged to double by partitioning, e.g. when doubling 56, double 50 (100) and then 6 (12) before combining (112). Partitioning non-canonically can also sometimes help when doubling, e.g. when doubling 63, double 50 (100) before doubling 13 (26) and recombining (126).
- Children may first investigate the patterns they notice in the digits that appear in a doubling sequence, e.g. when doubling 2

  (2, 4, 8, 16, 32, 64, 128 …) the last digits follow the pattern 2, 4, 8, 6, 2 … and when doubling 3 (3, 6, 12, 24, 48, 56 …) the last digits follow the pattern 6, 2, 4, 8, 6 … (apart from 3 itself).
- They may also notice that the same numbers appear in the sequences formed when doubling from different starting points. For example, when doubling 2 (2, 4, 8, 16, 32 …), 4 (4, 8, 16, 32 …), 8 (8, 16, 32 …).
- Children could also investigate how many doubles it takes to get above a certain number (e.g. 100) from different starting points. For example, when starting with 2, it takes 7 doubles, when starting with 3 it takes 6 doubles, when starting with 4 it takes 5 doubles etc.

Launching the activity

1. If available, read *One Grain of Rice* by Demi, or *The King's Chessboard* by David Birch, both of which revolve around constant doubling. These books could be read until the doubling problem is introduced/set.

2. Run a 'doubling race'. Give children one minute to constantly double, starting at the number 1, recording their answers on scrap paper or a whiteboard. Challenge them to see who can get the furthest.

3. Ask children to compare their doubling sequence with a partner and to discuss and compare their methods.

4. Discuss strategies for doubling with the class.

5. Share the problem poster, drawing attention to the 'things to think about' questions which children could investigate first.

6. Give children time to work on this problem in groups, simply answering, *What do you notice?* Children should ideally work using the graffiti maths technique. Support each group as needed, asking questions to develop reasoning and draw out patterns.

7. Towards the end of the session, reconvene the children. Invite each group to share something that they have noticed and to convince the rest of the class that they are correct.

8. If the session started with a 'doubling' book, the children could now be invited to solve the problem in the book, before reading the rest of it together as a class.

Developing reasoning

➤ *What do you notice* about this doubling sequence? About the number of doubles it takes to get over 100? Etc.

➤ *Convince me* that the pattern you have found exists.

➤ *What's the same? What's different* between the sequence formed when doubling starting at 2 and 16 (or 3 and 6, 14 and 7 etc.)?

➤ *Give me another starting number that would result in the same sequence. Another, another, another.*

➤ *Give me a **hard and easy** starting number. Why is this **hard and easy**?*

➤ *If we know the sequence formed when starting with 2, **what else do you know?***

➤ *Give me a **silly answer** to this the problem posed in the book. Why is it a silly answer?*

Providing differentiation

Support
A range of familiar representations and resources should be provided to support children in the calculation element of this activity. If doubling numbers becomes too challenging beyond 100, children could use a calculator to support the doubling, ensuring the focus remains on the reasoning and making generalisations.

Extension
The children could be encouraged to explore a wider range of starting numbers, including 3- and 4-digit starting numbers. The children could also be challenged to predict and then work out the number that would be formed by doubling different starting points 15 times, e.g. would starting with 4 produce double the answer when starting with 2?

 Key strategies

2 Another, another, another
3 Convince me
4 Hard and easy
9 Silly answers
11 What else do you know?

 Problem-solving approaches

Graffiti maths

Taking it further

This activity could lead into further investigations into patterns in numbers.

17 Fraction strips

Learning objective
- To investigate fractions, including fractions which are equivalent to each other.

Reasoning skills
- Working systematically
- Solving problems
- Conjecturing and convincing

Curriculum link
$\frac{1}{2}$ Fractions: investigate proportionality and equivalence in fractions

The problem

> Problem 17
>
> ## Fraction strips
>
> Cut up the sheet of strips from your teacher so that you have seven fraction strips.
>
> You could fold the strips to help show you different fractions. For example, you could easily fold your strip which has 3 sections marked on it into $\frac{1}{3}$ s.
>
> You could then use it and similar strips to help you answer different questions.
>
> **Your challenge**
>
> Fold strips so that they show:
>
> $\frac{1}{2}$ s $\frac{1}{4}$ s $\frac{1}{8}$ s $\frac{1}{3}$ s $\frac{1}{6}$ s $\frac{1}{5}$ s $\frac{1}{10}$ s
>
> **Then using your strips:**
> - **write sets of fractions that are equivalent to each other.**
> - **write number statements involving the addition and subtraction of fractions, e.g.** $\frac{1}{5} + \frac{2}{5} = \frac{3}{5}$
>
> **Things to think about:**
> - What do you notice about these fractions? Are any linked in any way?
> - How can you use your strips to prove that fractions are equal to each other?
> - How can you use your strips to help you make statements involving the addition and subtraction of fractions? Can you combine this with your knowledge of equivalent fractions to help you write more complex addition/subtraction statements?
>
> Year 4   *Problem Solving and Reasoning*

Background knowledge

- This investigation is based around the use of 'fraction strips', essentially strips of paper folded to show different fractions.
- The investigation aims to develop children's conceptual understanding of a fraction, and recap equivalencies and basic addition of fractions. Children will have been introduced to these concepts, in a basic form, in Year 3.
- It is important children understand that fractions represent a proportion of something. If the strip is folded to show $\frac{1}{5}$ it shows $\frac{1}{5}$ of the strip.
- Children need to know the mathematical terms and meaning of each part of a fraction:

$\dfrac{2}{3}$ → Numerator - the number of these equal parts that we 'need'

→ Denominator - the number of equal parts the whole is split into.

- Resource sheet 17.1, Fraction strips has strips split into 3 and 7 sections only, with no strips split into multiples of 2. This is to ensure that the children develop a true conceptual understanding of what a fraction is, rather than simply folding/shading along the lines.
- Once children have created their fraction strips, they are asked to identify fractions that are equal to each other. They can do this by aligning the strips, and using the different folded section to create equivalent fractions statements.
- Children are also asked to consider the addition of fractions. At this stage, most children will be expected to understand the addition of fractions with the same denominator (e.g. $\frac{1}{6} + \frac{2}{6} = \frac{3}{6}$), with most being able to recognise equivalent fractions in their addition statements (e.g. $\frac{1}{6} + \frac{2}{6} = \frac{1}{2}$, or for the most able, $\frac{1}{6} + \frac{1}{3} = \frac{1}{2}$).

Launching the activity

1. Give each child a copy of Resource sheet 17.1, Fraction strips. Introduce the problem by sharing the prompt poster. Stop at the first challenge, folding the strips to show the different fractions.

2. Recap the meaning of a fraction. Ask children to discuss in their pairs, *What is a fraction?* and then discuss this as a class. Ensure that children understand that a fraction represents a proportion and also know what each part denotes.

3. Give children time to fold their strips to represent the fractions shown. Encourage them to discuss any difficulties in pairs.

4. If children struggle with the fractions where there is no strip split into 'helpful' sections, revisit the meaning of a fraction being a proportion, and ask if, therefore, the lines really matter. See Developing reasoning (below) for more questions to ask during any moments of cognitive conflict.

5. Once children have folded their strips, introduce the other two challenges from the poster. Ask them to work on these in pairs, and support groups as needed, pulling small groups together if necessary to recap equivalent fractions and/or addition of fractions.

6. Towards the end of the session bring the children back together to share their learning and reasoning.

Developing reasoning

➤ **What do you notice** about the fraction (x)? How is this linked to?
➤ **Convince me** that this strip shows (x).
➤ **What's the same? What's different** between $\frac{1}{5}$ and $\frac{1}{10}$? $\frac{1}{3}$ and $\frac{1}{6}$? $\frac{1}{6}$, $\frac{1}{4}$ and $\frac{1}{2}$?
➤ *Give me a fraction that is equal to (x).* **Another, another, another.**

➤ *Give me a **hard and easy** fraction to fold these strips into. Why is it hard/easy?*
➤ *Which is the **odd one out** between these fractions? Why?*

Providing differentiation

Support
Children who are struggling with the concept of a fraction will benefit from spending an extended period of time on the first part of the activity (folding the fraction strips).

Extension
Children should be encouraged to make more complex addition/subtraction statements which use their knowledge of equivalent fractions (see example in Background knowledge).

 Key strategies

2 Another, another, another
3 Convince me
4 Hard and easy
10 What do you notice?
11 What else do you know?

 Problem-solving approaches

Paired work; think, pair, share

Taking it further

This activity could lead into further investigations involving fractions, including Investigation 6, Would you rather?

18 Birthdays

Learning objective
- To answer questions by collecting and interpreting data.

Reasoning skills
- Solving problems
- Making comparisons

Curriculum link
x= Statistics: collect and interpret data

The problem

Problem 18

Birthdays

You will need a class list for Key Stage 2 for your school which shows everyone's birthdays.

What will you find if you look at each month everyone in Key Stage 2 was born in?

Will you find that there are roughly the same number of children born in each month?

How could you show the data that you collect?

Things to think about:
- How are you going to collect your data and organise it?
- What is the best way to present your data?
- What does your data tell you?

Your challenge

Investigate the most popular month for birthdays in Key Stage 2 in your school.

Present your findings in a way that is helpful for other people.

RISING STARS
Maths

Year 4   Problem Solving and Reasoning

Background knowledge

- The children are asked to use an existing data set to investigate a statement made about the distribution of birth months.
- To complete this investigation, the children will need a copy of the class lists for your school, which include children's dates of birth.
- The problem asks the children to investigate the most common birth month at KS2. Depending on the size of the school and the ability of the children, this 'sample size' may need to be increased or decreased.
- The children will need to consider the best way to collect this data from the existing data set, e.g. a tally chart.

- The children will then need to consider how best to present this information. This may simply be in a table, or they may decide to present the data in a bar chart, which they may be able to create using ICT. ChartMaker Pro or apple numbers is an effective choice for tablets, Microsoft Excel or Google Sheets for computers, and http://nces.ed.gov/nceskids/createagraph/default.aspx and http://www.chartgo.com/ are both effective on-line chart makers.
- Once the children have collected the data, they should be encouraged to work out what else the data tells them, e.g. the number of children in the sample, the number of birthdays in each term etc.

Launching the activity

1. Begin by sharing the prompt poster with the children. Give them time to consider the challenge and to discuss with a partner their initial thoughts on how they could investigate the statement.

2. Share some of these initial thoughts as a class, drawing together any common themes.

3. Discuss how you may be able to use a data set already held by the school to help you investigate. Explain that you can provide them with class lists for KS2.

4. Ask the children how they could record the collection of the data from this data set, recapping how to create a tally chart or frequency table, as appropriate

5. Give the children time to work on the investigation, ideally in mixed ability groups. Support groups as needed, and discuss with each group, at the appropriate stage, how they may present their data and how they could interpret the data further.

6. At the end of the investigation, draw the class back together. Discuss their findings and what else they can tell from the data they have collected.

Developing reasoning

➤ **What do you notice** about the distribution of birth months?
➤ **What's the same? What's different** between a frequency table and a tally chart?
➤ Which year group is the **odd one out**? Why?
➤ **Convince me** that your findings are correct.

Providing differentiation

Support
The children may need to use a smaller sample size, or focus on another question which has fewer possible responses, e.g. the most popular house team, or term of birth etc.

Extension
The children can be challenged with a larger data set and should be encouraged to focus on the 'what else they can tell' element of the challenge.

 Key strategies

3 Convince me
7 Odd one out
9 Silly answers
10 What do you notice?
12 What's the same? What's different?

 Problem-solving approaches

Paired and group discussion

Taking it further

This investigation could be used as a springboard to explore further school data, or before children are asked to make and then investigate, their own data.

Glossary

Commutative An operation which can be carried out in any order without affecting the result. Addition and multiplication are commutative, e.g.
4 x 3 = 3 x 4 and 8 + 7 = 7 + 8.

Conjecture A thought or idea about a pattern, solution or relationship. Children should be encouraged to form conjectures about maths, e.g. 'My conjecture is that the answer will always be a product of the other numbers' and then to convince themselves and their peers that their conjecture is true.

Denominator The bottom number in a fraction. This shows how many equal parts the whole is split into.

Digit Digits are 0, 1, 2, 3, 4, 5, 6, 7, 8, 9. Their position within a number determines their value.

Digit root The number formed when continuously finding the digit sum until a single digit number is formed, e.g. the digit root of 789 is 6 (7 + 8 + 9 = 24, 2 + 4 = 6).

Digit sum The number formed when all the digits in a number are added (as if each digit were in the ones place), e.g. the digit sum of 789 is 24 (7 + 8 + 9).

Factor Factors of a number are numbers which multiply together to give that number and usually come in pairs, e.g. the factors of 24 are 1 and 24, 2 and 12, 3 and 8, 4 and 6.

Fraction A way of showing a proportion of a whole. Fractions take the form ½ and are made up of a numerator and denominator. A fraction splits the whole into equal parts.

Multiple A number which can be divided by another number without leaving a remainder, e.g. 6 is a multiple of 360 as 360 ÷ 6 = 60.

Number Numbers are digits which have been assigned a place value, e.g. the digits 3, 5 and 6 can be arranged to make the number 563 with the digit 5 having a value of 500 or 5 hundreds, the digit 6 having the value of 60 or 6 tens and the digit 3 having the value of 3 or 3 ones.

Numerator The top number in a fraction. This shows how many of the equal parts you 'have'.

Partitioning Breaking up a number into smaller numbers. Partitioning can be canonical, which means breaking multiples of 10, 100, 1000, etc (e.g. 878 partitioned canonically would be 800 + 70 + 8, or 400 + 400 + 70 + 8) or non-canonically which means partitioning into numbers which are not all multiples of 10, 100, 1000, etc (e.g. 878 = 450 + 350 + 35 + 35 + 6 + 2).

Polygon An enclosed shape with 3 or more straight sides. Regular polygons have equal sides and angles. Irregular polygons are those where the sides and angles differ in size.

Prime Prime numbers have only two factors: 1 and the number itself.

Product The result when multiplying two or more numbers together, e.g. the product of 3, 4 and 2 is 24.

Quadrilateral A 4-sided polygon.

Rectangle A quadrilateral with 4 right angles and 2 pairs of equal and parallel sides. A square is a special type of rectangle with 4 equal sides.

Square numbers Square numbers have an odd number of factors, as they can be formed by multiplying a number by itself, e.g. 16 is a square number, as it is the product of 4 x 4.

Sum The total when adding two or more numbers together, e.g. the sum of 5 + 6 is 11. 'Sums' do not refer to any type of calculation other than addition.

Systematically The act of working in an ordered and considered way, especially when tackling a problem or investigation, e.g. when exploring numbers which sum to 100, a systematic way of working would be to start with 100 + 0, then 99 + 1, 98 + 2, 97 + 3, etc.